DANA
The Irrelevant Man

Books by Douglass Cater

The Fourth Branch of Government
Power in Washington
Dana: The Irrelevant Man

Co-author, with Marquis Childs:
Ethics in a Business Society

DANA

The

A NOVEL BY

Irrelevant Man

DOUGLASS CATER

McGRAW-HILL BOOK COMPANY
New York   St. Louis   San Francisco   Toronto
Düsseldorf   Mexico   Panama

DANA
THE IRRELEVANT MAN

Copyright © 1970 by Douglass Cater. All rights
reserved. Printed in the United States of America.
No part of this publication may be reproduced, stored
in a retrieval system, or transmitted, in any form or
by any means, electronic, mechanical, photocopying,
recording, or otherwise, without the prior
written permission of the publisher.

Library of Congress Catalog Card Number: 72-124136

FIRST EDITION

10221

Only the times are fictitious.

—Anon.

I have always believed that the long view of man's history will show that his destiny on earth is progress toward the good life. . . . This is an act of faith. We must not let ourselves be engulfed in the passing waves which obscure the current of progress. . . . The only deadly sin I know is cynicism.

—Henry Stimson

My own conclusion is that history is simply social development along the line of weakest resistance, and that in most cases the line of weakest resistance is found as unconsciously by society as by water. . . The inevitable isolation and disillusionment of a really strong mind—one that combines force with elevation—is to me the romance and tragedy of statesmanship.

—Henry Adams

DANA
The Irrelevant Man

I

MY name is David Bohun, the *h* being silent. Pronounced Boon. My relations would like to claim kinship with the Kentucky explorer. But I doubt it. Bohun ancestors, as far as we can trace, lacked the energy to venture beyond southside Virginia. I despise the name and would have changed it long ago except for my dear, slow-dying Dad. Now it's too late, what with my involvements.

All my life I have lived in terror of *déjà vu*. It began in a sickly childhood when, of a sudden, the glimpse of someone or an overheard fragment of conversation could stir faint remembrances and set my mind on a desperate effort to discover just when and where it happened before. Once started, the forced journey of recollection quickly became a nightmare. Each turning of memory's pages produced a further blank. My tortured brain began to seem like an empty pit with sanity clinging to its crumbling edges. I acquired the habit of going straight to bed in hopes that sleep would purge the memory cells. As I grew older and health-

1

ier, this phenomenon occurred less frequently, but still the terror lingers.

So it was that green spring day last month. Springtime is a fatal season for those affected with *déjà vu,* especially springtime in Washington when the miracle of rebirth gentles a city in sad need of being born again. Henry Adams wrote an apostrophe to Washington in springtime, how it takes on strange new beauty with the first burst of dogwood. This courtly, cruel city where Adams knew such loneliness.

Springtime is terror time for David Bohun, for it is then that I am most susceptible to lost memories. That is why I felt a sudden apprehension when, walking along the streets of Georgetown that golden Sunday morning, I glimpsed a young lady leaving church, lean, soft-leathery, a random ray of sunlight filtering through the new-budded trees to light her face. I did not know the face but there was something familiar in the magic triangle of eyes and mouth. She was smiling. It was a full-lipped, voluptuous, almost wanton smile and memory's eye turned inward.

But this time *déjà vu* held no terror. I knew full well where I had last seen that smile and on whose face. It was five springs ago and her name was Pascal and she was the nearest I've ever had to lover. But here is the real miracle: not only the act of remembering holds no terror but the memory itself has lost its cutting edge of pain. I remember Pascal Dana and all that went with her—calmly, with the vision of the professional voyeur that I am and always will be.

And there in the greening streets of Georgetown, I knew that the time had come to make an accounting for the mis-

2

sion I had failed. Time to go back to my notebooks, review the record of my years in the Dana household, and tell what happened as I tried to compose the portrait of Pascal's father. For I was to be the authorized biographer of Chester Dana. I hold an obligation to the dead man.

It is one of many obligations now, for in the years since Dana's death I have become a free-lance ghostwriter serving the needs in a city whose politicians never learned to write for themselves. This earns me a modest living, more modest than when I lived on Dana's largesse. I continue to reside in Georgetown only a few blocks from the Dana estate. But it is a different stratum of Georgetown, and I live in what is euphemistically called an English basement apartment. Now each day since that Sunday morning I work to sort out the memories and the notebook scribblings, hoping against hope that I can piece together the story which has obsessed me so long. And the place to begin is on another spring day five years ago which was the end of the story.

Anybody who was somebody was there that morning, filling the nave of the splendid National Cathedral and overflowing into the transepts. A battalion of ushers seated each according to his proper rank, Cabinet officers and Ambassadors in the forward rows, Senators and Congressmen and lesser potentates strung out behind. The Bishop himself, gaunt and grave, kept an eye on protocol. Shortly before the bell tolled the appointed hour, he ushered in the President surrounded by an anxious retinue of walkie-talkie secret-service men. While everyone watched, our nation's Chief

Executive murmured solemn words to the widow Dana, then took a seat across the aisle, every line of his tired face and sturdy physique conveying deep dejection.

The great choir sang and the Secretary of the Smithsonian read the Scriptures and the Chief Justice gave the eulogy. It was a stirring tribute to our departed hero. Success, the Chief Justice pointed out, had dogged Dana's path every step of the way through life. Success in his early academic years when this son of the South became the brilliant student at Harvard. Success in the stratospheric world of finance where he won his sizable fortune. Success in wartime service to the Pentagon. And then, when most men might have rested, success in his later career as government's great unpaid statesman, as "Counselor to Presidents." Dana was the preeminent President's man. The Chief Justice, speaking in his best orotund tones, seemed almost to challenge Heaven to match Dana's opportunity here on earth.

Famous men do not die every day in Washington, so the occasion must be made the most of. Compared, for instance, to our British brethren, we share little pageantry in this capital city which has grown into the world's great power center. What Henry Adams once called the dance of democracy is still mostly made up of the long queues where somber-suited men and their silk-frocked wives pass in review before the great and not-so-great. How can we magnify our majesty? A funeral provides fitting excuse for all the pomp that we deny our living heroes. So the powerful Cathedral organ pealed forth "A Mighty Fortress" and the U.S. Army Band closed the service with the surging "O God, Our Help in Ages Past."

4

And I stood far back in the Cathedral's shadowy recesses and thought that it was well. I do not know whether Chester Dana would have planned it that way. But David Bohun had planned it that way—planned the seating pattern, summoned the Bishop, notified the White House with a word of special pleading on the widow's behalf, recruited the Army Band, and ghosted the Chief Justice's eulogy. Yes, I was the real ghost at the funeral. Those eloquent words of tribute were the least I could offer after almost three years in Dana's service and not a single word of my own to show as result. Subsidized by the Dana fortune and taken into the Dana household as a year-round ghost at the banquet table, I had failed to produce one page of manuscript.

But it was a splendid funeral I produced and the widow Dana at least had cause to be grateful. As the cortege filed out of the Cathedral, coming close to where I stood just inside the great north portico, she raised her head and nodded, her dark veil not quite concealing the tense lines of her face and the fiery red hair. She had built a long career of her own around this successful man. Now he was gone. For one brief moment, the widow Dana must have been wondering what was to become of her.

I had no cause for a single moment's wonder. Free at last! Free at last! Lord God Almighty, free at last from the long captivity. This man I could love and hate with almost equal passion was safely beneath the soil in Arlington. I followed him there and listened while they blew the bugles and fired the muskets. I saw him lowered into the ugly red clay dirt of Virginia. From dust to dust, Chester Edward Dana is back where he came from unless someone switched

5

bodies in the coffin and saved him to haunt me for a few more years. There is irony in that: I was the ghost, but it was Dana who haunted me—biographer, gentleman's companion, nursemaid, and all-round factotum in the Dana menage. Among my duties, I also served as the lover and the cuckold, if someone who is unwed can be cuckolded.

That morning I turned to leave the gravesite as the clerics did their final putterings over the mortal remains of Chester Dana. And there she was, standing well back from the others, no veil shading her from the indecent sunlight that streamed down through the leafing oaks. I had not seen her at the Cathedral. Indeed, my scenario had contained no role for her. Dana did not need his daughter to celebrate this day. Yet there she stood, slim, young, the sun making a mock halo over the golden head. Those gray, gray eyes were pensive, remote in the soft tanned face. Then she caught my stare and her full-blown mouth, that wanton, voluptuary's mouth, lifted its corners in a smile. She was smiling. Pascal was smiling at her father's funeral.

How to describe my sensations? Like the rude tearing off of the clotted bandage over a freshly scabbed wound. Like instant dystrophy of the muscles so that each body movement, each gesture, each facial expression becomes an awkward agony. My path lay close by where she stood and somehow I numbed my way past, not knowing whether I gave a grin or grimace in reply. She reached a gloved hand into her purse and thrust on me a small envelope. Not till I had made my way down the steep slope through the stone hedgerows marking men who died for their country did I pause to open it. On the thick ivory parchment under an

6

ornate line drawing, her scrawled message was brief: *Come to me when you feel like it. P*

Something about the drawing caught my eye, an intricate curving of lines which seemed at first glance merely designed for decoration. Within this maze, two recumbent figures could be made out. They were male and female, engaged in coupling. Good girl, Pascal! A quick shiver of lust surged in my loins but then higher up my senses played dead. Standing beside my car, I memorized her message, crumpled the precious parchment and left it on Arlington's lovely green lawn.

7

II

"YOUNG man, they tell me you know how to put words on paper."

If Dana's funeral was the ending, this crude and cryptic approach marked the beginning nearly three years earlier. The old woman I later came to call, behind her back, "Dame" Dana had sought me out in my lair in Harvard's Adams House where I had begun my summer's work. She came one hot day, her approach heralded by a terse message which the janitor had slipped under my door. "A dame who says she is Chester Dana's wife phoned and wants to see you at three this afternoon." She sat there bolt upright, large, horselike, with flesh and wrinkles carefully camouflaging what had once been a handsome face. She had a bush of red hair that showed signs of being touched up. Her blunt, let's-don't-mince-words approach was obviously the product of many years' cultivation.

She had heard of me from an old professor friend whose judgment she respected. I was woefully inexperienced for the mission she had in mind, but maybe youth had its virtues. She doubted it. She would have preferred someone who knew his way round modern-day Washington. Still, Washington was full of lazy-ass writers (yes, she said lazy-ass, watching me carefully to see whether I blinked or blanched) and she would rather take chances with someone who could learn as he went along. Dame Dana's voice was dry and harsh. I remember wondering if she spoke to Presidents that way. I wondered, too, if after you got to know her she was always so intense, so driven, so thoroughly dislikable; wondered whether Chester Dana could really love and cherish this buzz saw of a wife.

She came to the point. Her husband was not getting any younger. Since somebody was bound to write his life sooner or later, she saw no reason why it shouldn't be done right while he was still around to lend a helping hand. She had known too many famous men whose careers were gutted by inept biographers. Would I be willing to undertake the life of Chester Dana? Not too subtly, she made clear that pay and working conditions would be satisfactory.

Later on, I learned that other factors beside my capacity to put words on paper had been involved in this invitation: Dana and I were both from the South, both white, Anglo-Saxon Protestants (she had been thrown off momentarily by genealogical suspicions of Bohun), had both studied at Harvard. She had read the reviews supplied by her professor friend of my single published work, a miserable treatise entitled *The Washington World of Henry Adams* for which there had been the standard academic accolades of "sensitive," "perceptive," "penetrating." She had taken the trouble to read the treatise herself, discovering that it was unabashedly admiring of Adams, the longtime observer in the

9

capital city. Perhaps she reasoned that some qualities of that brilliant commentator and historian might have rubbed off on me. Perhaps Dame Dana had motives that even she did not fully understand.

My own motives were likewise mixed. I was sick of Harvard, sick to death of unending academic drudgery which stretched both fore and aft as far as the eye could see, sick of the countless hours of probing books for the minutiae that make up historical research, sick of the crazy-quilt pattern one must piece together to fashion a scholarly career. Somewhere along the way I had lost my zest for scholarship. I had had a bellyful—and a brainful—of cold, lifeless ideas in the abstract. I was ready to move on. Going to Washington, where red-blooded men and living, breathing ideas had a happy meeting ground, seemed like the ideal avenue of escape for David Bohun.

My life has been much given to acting on impulse. Other men, I have observed, have a braking mechanism, an inner set of cautions that allows them to hold impulse in rein. But not Bohun. Dangle an opportunity before me and I jump clear out of the water to seize it. Try as I may, I can recall no presentiments of doom during that hot summer afternoon. Chester Dana was to be my quarry and I knew enough of his fame and fortune to have no premature doubts. Before his wife had left my study, the bargain was as good as sealed. Only when she was safely gone did it occur to me to wonder whether her husband was a willing partner in this enterprise.

Now, nearly eight years later, I still wonder. Here in my basement room, I am playing solitaire with the pages of my notebook searching for clues not only to this but to many of the mysteries about the life of Chester Dana. It may be an idle pursuit to shuffle these scraps in the hope they can be fitted into a coherent whole. But it is the only way I know how to move ahead after so long a period of stagnation.

My very first notebook entry was made a few days after that talk with Dame Dana. It followed a brief visit to the Dana summer home in the village of Pride's Crossing, north of Boston. Imitative of my hero Henry Adams, I affected the third person in my journals. For brevity's sake, I employed only my initial:

At Mrs. D's suggestion, B takes the afternoon train. Met at the station by a taciturn old fellow in chauffeur's cap and driven in paneled station wagon along the winding road to Dana estate, "The Bluffs." This is rich man's territory and old CD is king of the hillside. A good country mile from the iron entrance gate to the austere Norman mansion on a high promontory commanding a sweep of the ocean.

How smoothly the rich people live! If this is the way they rough it on vacations, what must life in the city be like? Maids and butlers move unobtrusively to serve their needs, then disappear into the cubbyholes where they spend their waiting hours. Dame Dana joins B on the graveled terrace just outside the living room. (Is it called "living room" in a rich man's house?) A little less driven, a wee bit gentler in her native habitat. Still she seems apprehensive.

11

Is she still sizing up this fellow Bohun—an uncommonly gaunt young man with his unruly hair and that sharp beak of a nose? Dressed in subdued Navy-blue blazer and gray trousers. But maybe the crimson ascot is too much. All evening it clings around his neck in acute discomfort. B must remind himself that the amanuensis in this household, like the good butler, should be not seen and not heard.

Dana having his afternoon nap. Presently he comes up, moving quietly out onto the terrace, tall, aristocratic, a fine head, firm clear skin, strong chin, and that straight Grecian nose. Fascinated by the eyes, cold blue-gray, peering out from beneath those bristling brows. Age has weathered him but not harshly. Even in repose, he carries a lanky, lean-muscled strength. The voice is striking—rich, fluid, with almost melodious resonance. Traces of southernisms show through but only traces and of the upper South. He speaks softly as if long accustomed to being heard without having to shout.

Dressed in vacation attire, he conveys an elegance, an air of distinction. But he does not appear to be posing, simply living out a style of life to which he is accustomed. His only seeming concessions to conceit are those eyebrows, iron-gray, which offset the cropped mass of iron-gray hair on top his head. Does a man decide consciously to affect eyebrows like that? He must brush them.

Is there a protocol for biographers on first meeting their intendeds? B finds himself sniffing around Dana like toy terrier around great Dane. A tall man, a long-legged tallness that adds extra dignity to his carriage. He generates a curious ambiance —an atmosphere of aloofness, detached, cool, a way of lapsing into reverie and suddenly arousing himself out of it. He is not, B must reassure himself, unfriendly.

Dana ready for his constitutional and the next hour B gets a workout to which he is severely unaccustomed. Also gets a tour of Pride's Crossing. Place named after a nephew of the Cromwell lieutenant who signed the death warrant of King Charles I. But its present residents, Dana notes with irony, do not glory in this regicidal tradition. Dana, a man of ironies, points out a thicket known as Witch Wood. Got its name when a long-ago citizen was sentenced to be executed for witchcraft. Given a stay to say farewell to his family in Gloucester. Took a shortcut through these woods. Made the round trip so speedily that everybody regarded it as further proof of guilt. So the poor fellow was garroted.

More irony. We pass a stretch known as Mingo Beach. Back in eighteenth century, Dana tells B, a slave named Mingo was promised freedom by his master if ever the tide ran so low that he could walk out to the ledge lying offshore. By freakish phenomenon, the tide actually got that low in 1773—the very year old Mingo died.

As they hike back home, Dana makes brief reference to the biographical assignment. "My wife can be a determined woman. It won't hurt anything if

13

we have a try at it." That's all. He seems slightly embarrassed.

Much taken by Dana even though the first evening does not go all that easily. Move from cocktails to dinner and then to coffee before the fire with frequent lapses into silence. Dame Dana does little to help out. Maybe she wishes to test how well B can cope for himself. Or maybe—the odd thought crosses B's mind—she is not entirely comfortable in the presence of her husband.

That is as far as my notes on the first meeting go. They fail miserably to catch the mood of that evening or the mystique of the man. Nor do they reflect the excitement I felt over what lay ahead. For, within my free-wheeling imagination, I had already ventured well beyond the stately little journey being offered me. I would go to Washington all right, but not just to record the memoirs of Chester Dana. Like my famous nonrelation, Daniel Boone, I would be engaged in exploration. Only mine would be a journey along new frontiers of the interior. I was already, in my mind's egotistical eye, the latter-day Henry Adams, serving as voyeur in the nation's capital just as old Henry did, portraying the life and movement and feel of politics. I would be like the heroine in Adams' novel *Democracy*: "She wanted to see with her own eyes the action of primary forces; to touch with her own hand the massive machinery of society; to measure with her own mind the capacity of the motive power. She was bent upon getting to the heart of the great American mystery of democracy and government. She cared little where her pursuit might lead her. . . ." My story

14

would be about a different Washington, not a sleepy little Southern town on the Potomac but a great metropolis; not the capital of a still-new and weakly nation but one whose power stretches everywhere.

It pains me more than I can bear to describe these vaulting ambitions but that is the way it was. When I signed on that evening in Pride's Crossing, I planned to write the story of Chester Dana, yet all the while I would be seeking anew to trace the magnetic forces of history, to define Power, to comprehend the true meaning of the universe. Adams was always comparing the "order" of the thirteenth century with the growing "disorder" of the nineteenth. I had even starker comparison to make.

I would write the success story of Chester Dana but search for failures, too. I meant to be more intimate than a valet to this man's inner self. I would probe his psyche and turn up secrets such as no biographer had ever done before. Something more than intuition told me there was opportunity here, some half-remembered rumor that cast a faint shadow on his all-too-glittering saga. Had Chester Dana's career really been a success? I did not know the answer, but all the powers were not going to prevent me from finding out.

I was quite orderly in my mind at the time. If my design seemed subversive of the purpose for which Dame Dana hired me, let it be. I believed that the historian has a higher loyalty than to his subject. For this loyalty the biographer is obliged to endure much. He must even play the knave's role at times, ferreting out the truth while concealing his motives and masking his mission. He must not, I believed, imitate the journalist who exposes the politician one day and

15

shamelessly panders to him the next. He has a more serious assignment than pecking out a hurried first draft of history, committing errors of fact and insight in the haste to rush his chronicle into print. Mine was to be a more painful assignment, demanding time and patience and persistence. I had no idea how long this journey with Chester Dana would take but I was determined not to be hurried.

These were the thoughts that moved through my mind during that first evening at Pride's Crossing and provided a counterpoint to the conversation. Now, after all these years in this prison I designed for myself, my ambition comes back to haunt me. On what did I feed that I could be so arrogant? Did I really believe that I could plumb a man's life? And, if I did, could I hope to find the right words and put them in the right sequence to make a coherent story? Of my Adamsian ambitions to comprehend the wider world of Washington and to construct a theory of history, the less said the better. All I have are my notes. My task is to reduce them to the essential elements. Like my predecessor Adams, I must keep trying to get my education to begin.

One unrecorded memory of that evening. During a moment's privacy before we went in to dinner, I stood in the hallway and studied the large oil portrait of two children in their early teens. A handsome pair. I learned they were the Dana son and daughter painted a decade earlier. The boy was tall, slim, blond, blue-eyed, still youthfully tender. But it was the girl, smaller, younger, who attracted my eye. Her body was still a child's but something about the face suggested the woman that was to be. I remember wondering what sort of woman she had grown into. I speculated with

16

a male's curiosity how well I would get to know the Dana daughter. But then it was only idle curiosity.

One other memory of that evening lingers in my mind. After dinner, the silences grew longer as we sat in the large room's semi-darkness and Dana indulged his private musings. Before the fire, Dame Dana appeared to doze, her wrinkles relaxing into the tired hammock of her face. In the distance, a ship played a dreary monotone on its fog horn. During the lapses between, another sound could be heard repeatedly and close at hand. Suddenly, it came to me what it was. Gently, almost wistfully, Dame Dana was passing wind.

III

I WENT for a walk this morning and, nearly as a stranger, peered through the gate opening into the Dana grounds. Time began for me there almost eight years ago—A.D. 1, Anno Danae one—as if all that had gone before had led up to this and all that would come after had no meaning. While the Danas were still away in Pride's Crossing, I moved into the quaint gatekeeper's cottage where I could serve as lonely sentinel for all who came and went. Upon their return in September, I habitually took my evening meal with them and shared the salon that Dame Dana worked so hard to maintain. Their Georgetown estate was, if possible, more grand than the one at Pride's Crossing. A stately red-brick Georgian mansion set well back from the street, it opened to the rear onto a set of terraces where swimming pool and tennis court were nearly hidden amid the great oaks and boxwood hedges. A man could take a day's hike through that garden without retracing his steps. In the house itself, there was a blending of the contemporary with the antique

18

to bring grace to its high-ceilinged chambers. This was an airy cheerful house and on first wandering through my spirits too were cheerful. I had no way of knowing then that one can build a dungeon for oneself in the midst of the most pleasant surroundings.

My research for the biography of Chester Dana had good and bad beginnings. Good in having rich resources to piece together the public narrative. All that hot August I occupied a tiny cubicle in the Library of Congress and worked my way through stacks of newspapers and magazines searching for the nuggets of Dana lore. They provided a full if not overly rewarding haul. Dana had had blessed treatment in the press. So far as I could find, he had made no enemies among the reporters; on the contrary, he enjoyed the happy fate of many just outside official government of being accorded role without responsibility. Slowly over time, I could trace the plagiarism of the press as one anecdote after another got picked up and repeated, each story building on and buttressing the one before. Reviewing this chronicle, I could understand why the public legend of Chester Dana had reached such massive dimensions.

But I also soon discovered that the private legend would be more difficult to come by. For Dana was the prototype of the shadow statesman in the age of the telephone. He maintained few records of consequence. He kept no journal. He published nothing. As his career stretched serenely into the past, it was going to be hard to get a hook into. And I meant to put my hooks in deep, even at the risk of upsetting the plans I suspected that Dame Dana had for me. By the time they returned from their summer in Pride's Crossing, my notebook already contained the first rough

19

outlines of that public legend and the first question marks
for the chapters I wanted to explore further:

*Chester Dana hails from blue-blooded beginnings
in the South, heir to a distinguished line of lawyers,
judges, and Episcopal churchmen who played leading roles in the life of Virginia. His immediate family not wealthy but well-off. Father died when Dana
still young. Reared by mother; showed early aptitude as a student. First of his family not to take
traditional route to the University at Charlottesville.
Instead, went north to Harvard.*

[*DB: What happened to the old man? And why
Harvard?*]

*Majored in history and economics, won high
marks as scholar, made Phi Beta Kappa, and, quite
exceptional for a first-generation Harvard man,
taken into the Porcellian Club. Graduated near the
top of his class and offered a fellowship for continuing graduate studies.*

[*DB: Maybe Harvard changed before you got
there but what was Dana doing in the snobbish Pig
Club?*]

*Despite the lure of academia, he chose instead to
make his career in finance. Apprenticed at the re-
nowned Brown Brothers' Bank and, after a short
time, set out for himself as independent investment
counselor. By his late thirties, had made himself
many times a millionaire. In Wall Street, he soon established his great talent as a simplifier, bringing to
complex financial affairs the soft-spoken, almost*

20

simple language and logic of the Southern aristocrat in Yankeeland. But his outward mannerisms were deceptive, according to those who had dealings with him, for he carried little dead weight of Southern heritage or Ivy League training. Amid the sharp wheelings and dealings, he more than held his own with a capacity for shrewd hard-headed analysis and strong faith in his own intuition.

Dana's "intuition" became a legend both feared and venerated in the financial community. Rumors that he had psychic powers. A stray piece of intelligence could set his antennae quivering long ahead of his colleagues'. A few statistics, so the story goes, warned Dana of the coming crash on Wall Street. He passed through that catastrophe without a scratch. A chance conversation with a Jewish exile from Germany convinced him that the Second World War was on its way. He maneuvered his investments accordingly. No one could explain it; his followers were quite content to believe in divination.

[DB: Did CD have psychic powers or was he simply a good self-promoter? Need more about the crash of 1929.]

During his rapid rise in New York, Chester Dana took a wife, the former Emily Rockwell of Boston and Pride's Crossing, whose family had long been involved in the manufacture of textiles in New England. Blessed with two offspring: a daughter Pascal, now enrolled in Sweetbriar College, Virginia, and a son, Peter, deceased.

[DB: How did Peter die?]

21

Having missed military service during the First World War, Dana volunteered early for the Second. Soon elevated to an important staff post in the War Department where, among other activities, he advised on the Army's financial involvements in Europe. Won the respect of old War Secretary Henry Stimson. When the fighting ended, Dana—like so many others—never left town. His investment portfolio was sound and continued to grow with the nation's postwar growth. With no financial worries, he settled into a second career as adviser of government.

Washington was Dana's city. He purchased the Georgetown mansion which, under Emily Dana's sponsorship, became gathering place for many of the leaders on the postwar scene. An austere man, not given to revealing himself freely, he soon acquired a reputation as an éminence grise. He measured his words. Others, taking account of his brevity, came to value him more. His wisdom in finance proved readily transferable to the complex economic problems confronting postwar Washington. His capacity to simplify—to reduce the most intricate problem to homespun analogy—was an uncommon gift. He knew how to talk to politicians, to be reticent but persuasive. And he had a habit of not speaking till spoken to, indeed until urged to voice his views on the issue at hand. This was a strategem employed to good effect when time after time a high council wended its dreary way around the conference table while Dana remained imper-

*turbable and self-contained, his gray-blue eyes
seemingly looking inward beneath the bristling eyebrows. The results were predictable. At last the
presiding officer would notice the silent one in their
midst. "Perhaps Mr. Dana would comment on that
point?" Deliberately, as if time were of no moment
to him or to the harassed officials present, Dana
chose each word of response. "Mr. Chairman, there
is an old saying where I come from . . ."*

*His analogies were apt, often sharply puncturing
the banalities that had dominated the discussion.
They were uttered in a courtly manner and they seldom left a bitter taste. Admirers claimed he had a
rare talent for getting to the heart of the matter.*

*[DB: Surely at least one insider hated Dana's
guts?]*

*Chester Dana advanced to the highest ranks of
advice-givers. He had substituted on one occasion
for a Pentagon superior in testifying before Senator
Truman's Defense Committee. The matter involved
the transfer into French currency of tens of millions
of dollars and was potentially embarrassing to the
military. Slowly, softly, his bushy eyebrows impeccably brushed, Dana explained the predicament. He
conceded forthrightly that the French got the better
of that particular deal. But he lifted the Senators'
vision to a higher level and a more distant goal of
Allied unity. When Dana was finished the usually
tart Chairman had kind words to say about his testimony. After that, the War Department used him
frequently on Capitol Hill. Several times he served*

23

as emissary to Chairman Truman on matters that needed to avoid public airing.

[DB: Story moving too smoothly. Dana must have paid a price for moving into the big time?]

So it was that Chester Dana became an unpaid adviser of Presidents without regard to party. He never appeared to reach for his role. In fact, Washington parlor gossip had it that he was offered and refused more substantial jobs in government. Yet always when the President called, he was available. And the consultations broadened over the years to include the most far-reaching affairs of state. He maintained a sealed-lip security toward these consultations but occasionally an episode would leak out. There is a story, grown ornate in the retelling, of the time when trouble brewed in the tiny African country, Mozambia, which the geopoliticians had labeled the "hinge" to the continent. One tribal faction, abetted with munitions of Communist origin, was bent on obliterating another. Out of the bowels of the Pentagon emerged a plan for a swift air strike, to be conducted ostensibly by a neighbor country, which would "stomp out" the trouble before it grew serious. Officials in the State Department were inclined to go along. The plan, bearing the code name Operation Snipe, had moved toward final preparation when the President summoned Dana to a small gathering of his chief advisers.

Again the familiar marathon took place around the Cabinet table. Again each man strove to have

24

his say, the officials buttressing their views by reference to charts and voluminous staff papers. As usual, Chester Dana sat silent, almost studiedly removed from the fray, until the President at last nodded in his direction. Dana's drawl grows more extended with each narrator's retelling of the story: "Mr. President, if Mozambia is the 'hinge' country of Africa, I have only one question in the back of my mind. Suppose we make this strike at the hinge and suppose it succeeds. Which way will the other countries of Africa swing?" A quick tour of the conference table revealed that no one could address himself adequately to that point. Impatiently, the President adjourned the meeting with an acid request for a country-by-country assessment. And that was the last of Operation Snipe. In its place, the military managed to sneak a few arms to a friendly tribe and the little hinge country wound up in a neutral status.

It is remarkable how a single anecdote can be the making or breaking of a man in public life. The newspaper clippings on Dana contained one embroidery after another on this episode. But not until a long time later did I chance to come upon a column by a wire-service reporter which had not been carried in the big east-coast papers. It quoted an anonymous White House aide: "The President called that meeting because he had no intention of getting embroiled in an African misadventure. He counted on someone to raise an objection so he could scuttle 'Operation Snipe' without having to impose his formal veto. Dana played a key role, all right. Witting or not, he was the President's mouthpiece."

But there my outline of the public biography of Chester Dana broke off and there, if I had had any sense of gratitude, not to say honor, I should have let it end. Challenge enough to flesh out the details of this full career, to marshal the particulars about the policies Dana had helped to shape and the nation's crises he had struggled to avert. But, no, I was not content to take the hired biographer's route. David Bohun must create the unique biography, lifting the man out of his comfortable superficiality, measuring him for the eternal truths and falsehoods of his life. Something more was egging me on. As I sifted through the papers, read the clippings, followed the strands of rumor and myth, my suspicion began to grow. Beneath the smooth surface of success, failure had penetrated this man's career. Toward its climax there had been repeated rumors that he was to be appointed to the Cabinet, perhaps even be named Secretary of State. Then a whiff of discord was detected by the sensitive noses in Washington. There had been a break with the President, so the rumor ran. But a White House "source" had swiftly discredited the rumor. A photograph appeared in the newspapers showing a jovial Chief Executive seated at the Cabinet table and there at his right hand sat Chester Dana.

And that was that. Though the press took no more note, it marked the effective end of Dana's public career. There were no more speculations about a Cabinet post. Dana withdrew completely from serving as President's man. He settled into the quiet retirement which was his condition when I got my summons from Dame Dana.

A housebroken biographer would have left well enough alone. But I was young and this was my first big job. I had to know what had happened to cripple his career at its peak. The thought of attempting something less than the true life story of Dana never crossed my mind. Nor, I must confess in bitter retrospect, did I doubt that I had the capacity to judge this man.

IV

MY life in the Dana household, which began that fall, seemed at the outset an idyllic existence, living amid the luxury of great wealth, setting my own schedule and pace, free of urgent deadlines, at liberty to come and go as my fancy suited. No one sought to question my routines. I habitually rose late and breakfasted alone in my tiny gatekeeper's cottage, spent the day on my research, and, more often than not, dined with the Danas and their guests.

As the reincarnate Henry Adams come to Washington, I was eager to get the feel of the city and its inhabitants. Those early months produced for me the same sense of "continual intoxication" that Adams felt when he first arrived. Ambitiously, I began in my notebook a series of sketches and essays. I wished not so much to note precise events as to capture the feel and flavor of the nation's capital, the movement of history being recorded here, the forces at work, the eternal truths.

Dame Dana's salon was catholic in its clientele. So a young man by sitting still and watching intently could learn

28

a fair amount about Washington. At least twice during the week and always on Sundays, people came around. I used to wonder at first about their regularity. The food was not distinguished nor the hostess a gifted conversationalist. But then I concluded that social rituals like most things become a matter of habit. Politicians and public servants, having a horror of private idleness, would far rather waste an evening in someone else's living room than in their own. There is the herd instinct in this, a drawing together as the sun goes down in order to derive body warmth from one another. Still I marveled that harassed officials should so willingly add this extra stop to their day's frenetic schedule.

But come they did. Cabinet officers, Senators, White House aides, and others who participate in the drama of the nation's capital. And there they sat, Republicans and Democrats, Yankees and Southerners, conservatives and liberals, outside the cockpit of their daily conflict, exhibiting most of the time the civility to be expected in a drawing room. There were times when the tensions of the day stretched into the evening, or when alcohol stimulated sudden controversy between two combatants. But these were rare moments. Mostly the communicants at the Dana home were content to lay their burdens down and even to forget the roles they played so fiercely during the day.

Observing all this, I tried to begin my education in politics. One early entry in my notebook was devoted to Senator Vale, a good and liberally inclined man from the South who was frequent in attendance and seemed to be a favorite of Dana. From earliest childhood, I had heard tales of his political exploits. Entering Congress at a tender age, he survived one election after another and reached the highest

29

ranks of seniority while, back home, he kept the common touch by laying every cornerstone and dedicating every post office that federal largesse provides a senior Senator's constituency. In Washington, he grew to be a figure of power and reputation. There was a time, indeed, when Vale was ambitious for higher office. Such were his legislative good works and his fame as a political craftsman that he was chosen to be keynote speaker at his party's convention when the Vice-Presidential nomination was up for grabs. But before the assembled multitude and the millions more who huddled by their radio sets, Vale's performance came near to burlesque, his Southern accent thickening into a mush, his rhetoric throbbing with clichés. At that moment of glory and disaster, Vale's star started its descent. No one talked more about his dark-horse possibilities. As the years passed, it seemed remarkable that he could ever have been considered.

In the Dana home, I had the opportunity to study the Senator at close hand. It was a disconcerting experience, for even in the privacy of the drawing room Vale did not change. He was a compulsive talker, much given to repeating himself over and over and over again. He had a habit of ending an innocuous declaration with some such expression as "Yes, siree" and then, like a stuck gramophone record, trailing off with one "Yes, siree" after another till someone mercifully broke in. He loved to bestow terms of endearment like "Bless your heart" several times in the course of a conversation. I often felt a strong urge to grasp the Senator by the shoulders and shake him free from his nervous tic.

30

Once, at the end of a long-winded evening with Vale, I put the question to Dana: "Why does the Senator have to be so pompous?" Dana gave me a pellucid reply. "Pomposity," he said, "is the mask. Vale uses it to protect himself from his enemies." Over long decades of public service, Dana explained, this sensitive politician had been caught in an unbearable tension between his region's demands and the national interest as defined by his own convictions. Being a wise man as well as a good one, Vale came to understand that public utterances, no matter how eloquent, could never resolve this conflict. His instinct for survival taught him his ridiculous rhetoric. Habit hardened over time. He became inseparable from his mask.

Others who visited the Dana home showed less difficulty slipping in and out of their public masks. I remember being impressed by the dexterity of Senator Connar, a man Dame Dana liked but Dana only tolerated. He came from the Great Lakes region, a handsome young man, prematurely balding, with strong Jesuitical leanings and a style quite the opposite of Vale's. At the time Connar was building a nationwide reputation as a crusader at odds with his own party's leadership. A persistent gadfly to the President, Connar never held back publicly from "speaking the unspeakable." He was a regular on the TV interview programs and seldom a week went by that he did not claim his share of the news headlines. His words were free of pomposity, splendid in their witticisms and subtle, understated drolleries. His phrases, all pointing to the better America waiting to be born, quickly entered the nation's dialogue and were endlessly echoed. The commentators were uttering hopeful

31

words that a "new" politics of candor and concern might be emerging to replace the tired old politics of consensus and convenience.

After a vivid encounter at the Danas' I soon concluded that the private pose of this felicitous Senator was utterly different from his public one. Over coffee, Connar accosted a tired old Cabinet officer: "You profess to be moving heaven and earth to lick inflation," he accused. "But then you go and settle the automobile strike that would help deflation more than all your other policies put together." Irritably, the Cabinet officer responded that he didn't take any "unusual" steps to settle the auto strike. "Maybe not," said Connar, "but you could have taken steps to keep it from being settled." The Cabinet officer protested that this would have been a cynical thing to do. "It would have been the realistic thing to do," the Senator answered triumphantly. "You call me an idealist but I am a better realist than you are."

Later, in the hearing of a Presidential deputy, Connar referred to his recent defiance of the White House which the press had hailed as an "irreparable break." "If just once I had been listened to either on policies or appointments, all would have been forgiven," he said deliberately, conscious that these precise words would be swiftly carried to the White House. "Just once—on policy *or* appointments," he repeated. To my untrained ear, there was the sound of very ancient politics in this hint of blackmail.

Watching these men with their masks, I was led more and more to speculate on the nature of the calling they pursue. The politician, I concluded, has kinship to the artist. He must be capable of sensitivity far beyond the ordinary art-

32

ist's. While the artist works with oil and canvas and musical scores, the politician works with human beings. Yet he cannot be merely the sum of constituent noises; somehow he must strike the chords that combine those noises into a melodious whole. His is a thankless calling, despite the occasional glory. No politician is permitted the display of temperament that the public regularly accepts from the prima donnas in other artistic professions.

My notebooks recorded moments of drama around the Dana dinner table:

> *Listen in awe tonight as the middle-western Senator, Thomas Truesdale, long known as a leading militarist in Washington, recants a lifetime's convictions. For fifteen minutes, Truesdale holds his audience spellbound while he lambastes the faith in weaponry that was once his faith. He carries his argument further: The white man has no business in those parts of the world the colored man makes his habitat; indeed, the beginning of evil for Western man can be traced to Captain Cook's meddling among the dusky maids of Polynesia.*
>
> *When Truesdale finishes, the crusty ex-Secretary of State, Dudley Alcott, stirs himself from his musings. "Senator, what you have just said proves how right I was when I supported you for President many years ago." But the Senator's swell of pride is cut short. "Because if you were President, you would not dare utter the God-damned nonsense we have just listened to." Dana leads the laughter but Dame Dana does not seem amused.*

33

My sense of history was enormously stimulated by these random clashes. Another evening, which I failed to record but will never forget, a notable old bore tried to interrogate ex-Secretary Alcott, who carried the scars of many wars in Washington. Leaning halfway down the table and seizing a moment of silence so that all could hear, the old bore called out, "Something I have always wondered, Mr. Secretary, is how the State Department accommodates the sex habits of visiting notables. Tell us, were you ever obliged to procure women when the King of Arabia came to town?" For a long, long moment the ex-Secretary fixed his tormentor with a stony stare. Then from his lips long harnessed to diplomatic nicety, two pent-up words emerged. "Fuck you," replied the dignified ex-Secretary. All the diners turned quickly to their partners in a magpie effort to pretend that nothing had happened.

These were light moments of the incessant dialogue in the Dana salon. Amid my eavesdropping, I was disappointed by how rarely the conversation among the politicians reached beyond the pedestrian. Men who by day were engaged in stormy controversy seemed content to subside by night. In their place, the women often took over. I detected in their exchanges a harshness of judgment their husbands seldom displayed. Why was this? I came to attribute it to the desperation of distaff lives in a city of famous men who, as someone said, married when they were very young.

That first winter I sought to compare the capital with the earlier one Henry Adams knew so well. Washington was no longer a one-industry town, or at least that industry had grown into a conglomerate. It was little more than a village

34

when Adams lived here. Not a terribly wealthy man by to-day's standards, he could build his mansion across the square from the White House. Now many men with much more money lived in the towering apartments along the tree-lined avenues, and conducted their business in the anti-septic office buildings rising all over this metropolis. All sorts of new men were coming to Washington.

I did not know how to accommodate these new worlds of Washington. The city was too big. There were too many players. Men performed their roles in too many guises. It was no longer sufficient to ask a man his occupation. Men called themselves lawyers who never touched a law book. The old-fashioned lobbyist was becoming pretty much a vanishing breed. New types had emerged to take his place. Now men were specialists in the art of persuasion— information processors, opinion analysts, systems designers, etc., etc., crowding into the city and making the familiar pilgrimage through government bureaus and Congressional hearing rooms. If scale was changed, the essential business of Washington remained what it was in Adams' time—to get laws passed and dollars spent. And politicians elected.

Adams in a year or two could immerse himself in the whole of scientific knowledge. In the Dana salon, a nuclear physicist cheerfully admitted to being obsolete at the age of forty. The democratic dialogue had grown so varied and technical as to overwhelm the most conscientious student. I overheard conversations between the politicians and the military men, playing parlor war games with multiheaded missiles capable of causing megadeaths to the enemy in miniseconds. But even though their language was more so-

35

phisticated, I concluded that most of these men had quite simple, old-fashioned pictures in their heads of the world they lived in.

Take Senator Edmund Wright, the gloomy veteran on the Foreign Relations Committee. He made no excuses for the fact that he yearned for a return to small America. One evening at the Danas, just back from a visit to Iceland, he gave the dinner company a long glowing account of life in this tiny neighbor country to the north, of how "uncomplicated" were its affairs, how much to be envied. "We could learn from those happy, blessed people," he said sadly.

"What could we learn, Edmund?" asked Dana in a mildly bantering tone. "How to manage an economy that barely supports two hundred thousand men, women, and children?"

"We are too infernally obsessed with getting and begetting," answered the Senator. "Why can't we slow things down? Why can't we leave well enough alone?"

Dana shrugged his shoulders, not bothering to pick up a conversation destined to go nowhere.

Columnist Henry Mann, a household intimate who took it upon himself to serve as my mentor, was living by quite a different picture. A small ferretlike fellow with narrow nose and slicked-back hair, he followed the familiar journalistic practice of drowning out conversation by his incessant monologues. It was said that he got his best stories by listening to himself. For him, America had become the last bastion of good holding out against an evil world. He was constantly exhorting the Dana audience to more heroic efforts at home and abroad. Did he really believe that the na-

36

tion could succeed against so many enemies, I once inquired of Mann. "Of course not, my dear boy," Mann answered with acerbity. "But like the courageous men of all ages, we must be prepared to die bravely."

I made a game of guessing at the picture each man carried in his head. There was Penn Warfield, a tall, stiff-necked reporter who had produced a daily column of exposé out of Washington for three decades. He lived in a world of stark blacks and whites. Warfield's conversation at the Dana dinner table was little different from his copy for his reading public. Unbending in attitude as in stature, he held that men were either good or bad. His picture had no room for mezzotints. I was reminded of the hellfire evangelists I had listened to during my boyhood.

I found his opposite in Charley Capper, an ancient political operative in Washington. For Capper, the world was composed of subtle grays. He told a story on himself one night about the time, while working at the Treasury, he had got advance information of a pending move against certain banks, including one which held his own account. What to do? Chuckling, Capper said he had resolved his moral dilemma by withdrawing *half* his deposits.

But I was interested in more than the images these men lived by. I craved to learn something about power. I tried to fashion a yardstick for measuring power but soon found that the effort was beyond me. Power came in too many varieties to be capable of comparison. It differed in its basic substance. There was the raw stuff, undiluted as bootleg whiskey, belonging to the potentates in Congress like Senators Vale and Wright. It could pack a wallop. A different

37

kind of power belonged to those advising the President. Quite brittle. Derived from being able to say the right word at the right place at the right time.

I was intrigued by watching the power of some who never served on a government payroll. Often to the Dana home came a familiar threesome—lawyer, society reporter, and Washington matron—who constituted an unbeatable power on behalf of "fair treatment for dumb animals." Time and again, they had defeated huge government bureaus which grew careless in using animals for scientific experiments. They knew how to touch the right levers and they had passion. The lawyer was nationally known as a civil libertarian but one evening I overheard him declare, "If anybody ever harms my dog, I'll kill him in cold blood."

I concluded that power could not be compared to energy. For the committee chairman in Congress, it was entirely static, a matter of place not of motion. Yet the President, despite widespread complaints that his power had grown out of all bounds, had to move constantly and much more frantically than his predecessors in order to stay on top.

Columnist Mann argued that power had become a hackneyed term used by second-rate journalists for explaining the motives of those who congregate in Washington. "Ego explains what happens far more than the lust for power," he told me one snowy night when I walked him to his Victorian town house on Massachusetts Avenue after a dinner party at the Danas'. "The almighty ego afflicts everybody in Washington, even the clergy. Do you know what happened this evening? Old Bishop Flye asked me if I had heard the

Flye Amendment to Lord Acton: 'If power corrupts, being out of power corrupts absolutely.' I had to tell the poor Bishop that I had written this precise same dictum in my column six years ago. You should have seen how crestfallen he looked. Thought he had invented something original for a change."

"Few men seek real power," Mann went on. "Few would know what to do if they got it. What they really yearn for is 'involvement'—and even more than that, for being *known* to be involved." Mann's lesson seemed to be demonstrated when I witnessed an exchange between a junior Senator and a President's aide at the Dana cocktail hour. The Senator demanded irately why the President had stolen his "idea" for a particular program. The President's aide said he wasn't aware that the Senator had a patent on the idea. Besides, he added, Presidential endorsement meant that the· idea now had a chance of success. "Which would you rather have, Senator," the President's aide asked, "the program itself or credit for the idea?" "Why, the credit, of course," the Senator replied candidly.

Mann was gleeful when I reported this encounter. He nodded his glossy head and winked significantly. "There you have it. Most politicians would far prefer to be thought powerful than actually to deal with the harsh choices. They wrangle endlessly over who claims paternity for anything that succeeds. But when something fails, they are quite content to pass the blame."

But why, I wondered, did so many of them aspire to be President? "They lack imagination, my dear boy. Pure and simple. No imagination," said Mann. "They haven't the foggiest notion of how they would comport themselves if they should ever enter that office. That's why we witness one President after another going through a period of shock when he finally finds himself up against the raw reality of power."

As I review my early notes, I am surprised how little Dana himself appeared in them. This was not for want of interest on my part. During the early months I felt an intense fascination amounting almost to love for this venerable man. Yes, it is possible to feel love for a great man simply because he is great and you are being accorded the privilege of watching his greatness at close hand. Journalists exhibit this weakness all the time. That is why many public men become skilled in revealing—or pretending to reveal—their private selves to selected members of the press. Voyeurism demands this special intimacy.

So it was that I reveled in the opportunity to rub shoulders with a man who had rubbed shoulders with Presidents at moments when history was being made. I used to give my imagination free rein in picturing what it was really like on the inside—really inside the inner sanctum of power. Such a romantic image I had fashioned of this inner sanctum. I fancied that these privileged insiders were men apart, communing with a separate wisdom. I could not imagine anyone I had ever known in ordinary life being suited for a position of great power. Perhaps this, too, was a failure of imagination.

This may sound foolish in the telling but it explains why I was not particularly dismayed at the beginning when I found it difficult to get beneath the surface of Chester Dana. For me, he was a figure of bronze and, by their very substance, bronzes are impenetrable. Dana moved among his guests with grace. After dinner, he passed his cigars and, on occasion, told his stories with becoming charm. He did not give the impression of holding back. Many times of an evening I had the feeling that I stood on the edge of a breakthrough as I silently watched and listened. Afterward, in the quiet of my gatekeeper's cottage, I faced a different reality in trying to record my notes.

Slowly, I came to accept the fact that there is a breed of men reaching high place in Washington whom one can know and know intimately and still not know. They are not silent men. In fact, they may spend much time in formal communication. They give freely of their minds and their energies. But still they do not give of themselves. They say little of their love, desire, faith, remorse, submission, revolt. They remain an enigma. What causes this condition I did not—do not—understand. But of one thing I was determined. I meant to get behind the bronze of Chester Dana.

V

BEFORE many months had passed in the first year, I had developed respect combined with distaste for the wife of Chester Dana. The Dame was such a tough old turkey, relentless, ever purposeful whether in serving mankind or planning the next sociable. Though she said very little, her nervous intensity dominated the home. She figured more conspicuously than her husband in my early notes.

A meeting this A.M. *of a Dame Dana committee. Notable movers and shakers in attendance so B gets permission to eavesdrop. At issue: how to raise the funds to launch the campaign to persuade the Congress to vote the money to accomplish the good that this committee so earnestly seeks. Several members present could finance the entire campaign with a single scrawl in the checkbook. Instead, a fund-raising ball is suggested. They promptly group themselves into subcommittees—food, entertainment, guest lists, etc.—happily taking on this drudgery in lieu of putting up the cash. Before the affair is done, many hours of valuable man- and woman-power will be expended, fabulous door prizes donated, and the services of potentates enlisted so that socialite and social climber can gather together for an evening.*

A lively discussion erupts over who shall be selected honorary chairman. Madam P suggests that they should "hit for the top" and find out whether the First Lady will lend her name. But there are guarded demurrers. Other names are put forward. Dame Dana finally breaks the impasse by suggesting that it might be less "political" to go after the Vice-President's wife. So it is agreed.

B can't help but be intrigued by the politics of do-goodism. How much is selfless idealism, how much simply nervous energy, boredom, desire to dominate? But he does not scoff. Clearly the stimulus for so much that is noble and generous in this nation comes from these earnest volunteers, who move incessantly from one meeting to another and spend their days with endless telephone lists. B hears Senator Vale pay tribute to the role of women on a recent evening while making an after-dinner toast to Dame Dana. "Whenever there is a good idea to be sponsored, a good cause to be promoted, a balky politician or bureaucrat to be prodded, cherchez la femme," *Vale concludes in ringing cadence.*

Henry Mann says one could construct an anatomy of do-goodism—how it commences with these volunteers, receives a boost from foundation

43

philanthropy, gets seized upon by eager Presidential agents, and finally becomes hardened into legislative statute. Then a different set of forces takes over. Shrewd lobbies rise up to protect this new program and, as time passes, the generous innovation turns into the cynical vested interest. So it is time for the volunteer do-gooders to commence again—the inevitable life cycle of a democracy.

Professor Alton Sharp, short, fat, and bespectacled, has come down from Harvard this morning to join Dame Dana's group. He is supposed to embody the notion that "ideas" are as important as "actions" in the group's effort to achieve progress for the nation. But the professor appears more preoccupied with tactics. He speaks of the vanity of Congressman X and venality of Chairman Y. He freely attributes a controlling motivation to each of the solons. "All we need to get Senator Purdy on our side is to stir up the Iowa chicken farmers," he declares. B wonders whether a member of Congress marches to a single tune. But the others present nod appreciatively at Professor Sharp's wisdom. This leads B to speculate about the survival of the good in a system where good and bad are locked in fierce combat. Is there any way to institutionalize the do-gooding, to place less of a burden on these volunteer groups like Dame Dana's who form the posses to combat the evildoers?

Watching this particular posse gathered in the Dana drawing room, B cannot escape the feeling that the system is fragile. Surely, good needs more

44

professional, all-purpose, round-the-clock defenders.
But B doubts he would select Dame Dana or her
colleagues to play this professional role. He finds in
them the same vanities that afflict the politicians.
And even greater arrogance. They seem so positive
they know precisely what is right and wrong, so in-
tolerant of others who may have different yard-
sticks.

Life around the Dana household moved to Dame Dana's
drumbeat. She planned the menu, made up the guest lists.
On those rare occasions when husband and wife went together without a chauffeur, she drove the car. It was an orderly household, but beneath the surface one felt that it was
a driven household with the old Dame never quite at ease,
never content to leave well enough alone. At the same time,
it was a curiously disconnected household. Husband and
wife moved most of the time in completely separate orbits.
I do not recall an instance when Chester Dana raised his
voice to his wife or let the faintest flicker of exasperation
mar his manners. Neither was there a single time when I,
the constant eavesdropper, overheard a word of endearment.

I have a clear picture in my mind of the two seated at
the breakfast table on the small garden terrace flooded with
flowers and sun, surely among the more intimate moments I
shared with them. Dana, ruddy, exuding early morning
freshness and shaving cologne, those eyebrows seeming to
acquire extra bristle after his slumber. The Dame, puffy,
heavy-lidded, looking aged under the fierce sunlight. She
compensated somewhat by the vigor of her breakfast move-

ments, the old man appearing almost languid by comparison. She read choice bits from the morning papers stacked, his and hers, at each place. " 'Senator Gordan left today for a swift inspection trip of NATO,' " she read, pince-nez held at nose length from her face. "Why, that bastard promised us he would get committee action on our wildlife bill this week." And Chester Dana, slowly, patiently, would look up from his own newspaper reading. "Possibly the Senator had a conflict of schedule, my dear. I doubt you will change his mind by questioning the legitimacy of his birth." Dana's voice was always cool and dry, always with a tone of resignation to her verbal excesses.

Why had passion gone out of the marriage? My researches tended to raise the more disturbing question whether passion had ever been there in the first place. Perhaps it is a prejudice of Southerners to suspect that beneath the cold exterior of the New Englander beats a heart of ice. Emily Dana's life, so far as I was able to reconstruct it, offered nothing to dispel this suspicion. I have an early childhood photograph of Emily, taken *en famille* during a summer outing at Pride's Crossing. Mother, father, six sons and daughters with Emily, at five, the youngest. All lean and lanky, dressed in simple vacation attire. All staring straight into the camera with no hint of horseplay, no sign that any one of them recognized the others' existence. Had there been a family quarrel just before the shutter clicked? Or was this the habitual pose of an austere textile dynasty now in its fourth generation?

Emily had been dispatched to the Farmington Academy at the age of eight and spent the better part of growing up away from home. Perhaps here the child cried out for a mother's love in the loneliness of the night and by day was taught to wear the stoic mask. She had learned to wear the mask well by the time they took the photograph for her senior yearbook. That album which I found tucked away on an upper shelf of the Dana library records two achievements for Emily Rockwell: Varsity Soccer Team and High Honors List. Beneath the tense visage of the teenager, her class editor had inscribed one glowing testimonial: "Miss Purposeful."

After considerable searching, I located the Farmington headmistress in charge during Dame Dana's years there. By now she was of advanced age but still possessing her faculties. A wiry old maid, she was waiting out her earthly existence in the tiny apartment of a converted brownstone on Boston's Beacon Hill. A tawny Siamese served as her sole companion and the place smelled of rose-petal sachet. Yes, she remembered Emily Rockwell quite distinctly. A talented girl, shy and somewhat withdrawn but obviously of superior fiber. (Is it significant that the New Englander talks of "fiber" when evaluating a child's pedigree whereas the Southerner speaks of "blood"? Perhaps one is concerned with strength and the other with spirit.) The headmistress had little more to contribute. She had known Emily would go far and always exemplify the best of the Farmington tradition. What was the best of the Farmington tradition? She shook her head impatiently as if to dismiss a foolish question. "Why, I suppose, the capacity to cope no matter what hardships or challenges life puts in one's way."

Emily went on to Radcliffe College in an era when Harvard men regarded Radcliffe women as insufferable grinds. Nothing I could find out about her stay there raised any

47

suspicion that she had deviated from the norm. Her roommate, now a portly Waltham matron, could add little beyond
the conventional clichés—"diligent," "hardworking," "occasional signs of a fierce ambition."

"No, I would not say that she seemed unduly afflicted
with a social conscience. She was a regular participant in
the Phillips Brooks House welfare work but I always suspected it was a way to keep busy and maybe meet a Harvard man. She was not exactly overwhelmed with suitors."
Emily and the roommate had not exchanged letters since
their farewells on graduation day.

The Rockwell daughter, now grown to nearly six feet,
had fared better than her roommate knew. On more than
one holiday weekend, her brother Tod brought to Pride's
Crossing his brother in Porcellian who could not get home
to Virginia. All those years later she found curious adjec-
tives to recreate her first impressions of young Chester
Dana: "courtly" "distinguished" "reserved." I once summoned up my courage and tried to prod deeper. Had she
known that this was her man and laid the tender trap for
him? Dame Dana gave a dry laugh of unamusement. "I
doubt if he thought about me twice the whole time he was
at Harvard."

Five years later Tod was killed in an automobile crash
and Dana returned to Pride's Crossing for the funeral. He
came back several times after that and Emily took time off
from her job as social worker in Boston to visit New York.
It was not a lengthy courtship. The wedding at Pride's
Crossing took place with only family present. Dana's
mother came up from Richmond and was the one person
there who wept real tears. The newlyweds made a trip to

Europe and soon returned so that Chester Dana could resume his climb up the New York financial ladder.

Where was the romance of this connubial venture? Surely that wedding night the fires burned bright as the courtly young man crushed the severe young maiden in his arms. There were fruits of their union. But try as I might in the ascetic aftermath these many years later, I could never call up a mental image of passion between the two. I came to accept a fact alien to my own experience, where love and hate were the mingled interplay of family life, that the Danas' had been a marriage of convenience, each taking the other till death do part because it suited a notion of one's own destiny. And, despite the vicissitudes and, more of a test, despite all the triumphs that marked their long life together, the marriage had worked.

Yet, even as I write these words, I find myself asking what is the definition of that word *worked*. Had the marriage worked so far as Pascal Dana was concerned? Or Peter Dana? Even to ask this question at this point means to get my story all jumbled up in the telling. It is enough to say that, no, I don't believe the marriage had worked for the Dana children. This is a harsh judgment. I make it nonetheless, for I am the biographer and a biographer must sometime play the role of God.

Perhaps this, too, does not fit into my story at this point, but it bears on Dana's attitude toward the opposite sex. It was told to me with traces of a leer by a retired life insurance executive who had for a time shared with Dana and two other classmates a large apartment on Harvard's Gold Coast. There had been at least one affair of passion in young Dana's life. "He was never much of a man for wild parties and all that, but I remember on a Saturday night he came in quite late when we had a good one going. There was this blonde there, a stunning thing who went to some kind of secretarial college in Boston. She and Dana took one look at each other. He spoke to her in the Southern way he had. The next thing we knew they were leaving the party together without so much as hail and farewell to the fellow who brought her."

The old roommate implied there had been a great deal more to it. Dana saw a lot of the girl that year. She was always hanging around the apartment, a quiet, shy creature but you could tell by the way she looked at Dana that lust lay just beneath the surface. With true Southern chivalry, Dana never alluded to his love life. But his roommates didn't need it spelled out what was going on. The year had passed and when Dana came back the following autumn the romance had apparently passed too. No, the retired life insurance executive couldn't remember the girl's name or what had ever happened to her. He doubted she was cut out for the kind of career that lay ahead of Dana.

But I, the hired biographer of Chester Dana, was not convinced by his doubt. In this nation's capital, there are many famous men and the women they married before the mingled yearnings had dried out. Distinguished Justices and Senators and Secretaries of State move through careers accompanied by squat, fat, flighty wives who once may have been pretty, once must have stirred such a torment of longing that holy wedlock seemed the only escape. Even now, when other passions have replaced the ones long ago, these men appear content with their lot. Even now, of a spring

50

evening, I have caught the exchange of tender glances between a hardened old politician and his frumpy *hausfrau,* signifying that love is not dead. Yet, watch as closely as I could, I never caught such an exchange between the Danas.

VI

EACH January, as I discovered that first winter at the Danas, a new life cycle begins in Washington at the opening of Congress. I dutifully paid a visit to the Capitol with columnist Henry Mann serving as my guide and commentator.

We lunched with Senator Connar, who took a special delight in deriding the "obsolescence" of the legislative branch. "We are bogged down in our petty prerogatives," he observed ruefully. "We are helpless against the cunning of the White House." Shaking his balding head, the Senator told us that he had given up any hope that Congress could act as a collective body to impose its will on the Executive. That is why he had committed himself to the path of private guerrilla warfare. "It annoys the President, intrigues the press and satisfies my constituents. That's good enough reason. Actually, it also annoys most of my esteemed colleagues but there's not a damn thing they can do about it."

I found myself rather smitten by all the antiquities of Congress. The ornately painted walls and ceilings, the great overstuffed black leather settees, the myriad busts, the incessant bustle in the corridors. There was a nineteenth-century smell about the place. But here the business of democracy appeared to be out in the open, not cooped up as it is in the bureaucratic rabbit warrens at the other end of town. I could understand why most reporters describe Congress with color and drama that they lack when they report the executive branch. My notes that night tried to capture the flavor of Capitol Hill:

> *Senate in a state of desuetude. Enormous idleness. Presiding officer engaging in lazy discussion with a clerk. Youthful pages reclining indolently on the steps below the dais. Senator Vale, long-haired and long-winded as always, drones through a prepared text supporting cotton subsidy. A half-dozen Senators on the floor, signing stacks of mail, reading newspapers, dozing. Visitors being systematically flushed through the galleries so that "the people" can watch their elected representatives at work. This is the marathon ceremony of Congress. Mann remarks that the world's greatest deliberative body must deliberate even when there is nothing to deliberate about.*
>
> *How does John Citizen regard this spectacle? B notices that a gaggle of women seated just beneath him in the gallery comes suddenly alive when a lanky man, the butt of a spent cigar in his mouth, appears between the swinging doors which lead from the cloak room. Their Senator has arrived. A buzz of excitement moves among the women. But*

53

the Senator, after blearily surveying the chamber, turns and disappears once more into the dark depths of the cloak room. The murmur dies away and B overhears a verdict from one woman: "He looked kinda seedy, didn't he?"

B relates the experience to Mann, questioning whether it wouldn't hurt the Senator's prospects back home. Mann makes light of it. Other things being equal, the American people would far rather have a Senator who sends them seed catalogues than one who makes great speeches in the Senate chamber.

B finds himself idly wondering how Chester Dana would fare as a Senator. He looks and acts the role far better than most Senators. But would he really want to put up with all the back-slapping and the hand-clasping? More importantly, could Dana, having crossed the Mason-Dixon Line, accept or be acceptable to the politics of his native state?

To the innocent observer, there is mystery in the way the Senate suddenly blossoms into life. Connar rises behind the small lectern placed on his desk, reporters hurriedly crowd into the press gallery, and, lo, other Senators appear from nowhere waiting expectantly for debate to get underway. Actually, Mann explains, it is all rather well planned. Notices have been sent out on the news wire that the Senator plans to deliver a blockbuster against the President at 3 P.M. sharp.

Here is the drama for which this august body is

54

*famed. Connar is well armed for this foray, having
been fed his facts, Mann says, by the President's
own disloyal deputies. He delivers his speech with
gusto, helped along by one or two colleagues who
offer him leading questions and react with appropriate expressions of shock, horror, and outrage at
each new revelation. It appears that the President
has callously ignored the expressed will of Congress. In the words of the prayer book, he has done
things he ought not to have done and left undone
things he ought to have done. To hear his accusers,
he has played fast and loose with the Constitution
of the United States of America.*

*Evidently the President's supporters have sized
up the attack and decided that silence is the best defense. Or it may be, Mann speculates, that they feel
it is a good thing to hold the President's feet to the
fire. The promised debate does not erupt. Instead,
the one-sided attack continues for a spell. Then, as
mysteriously as it begins, the excitement is over.
The Senators and the press withdraw, and the great
deliberative body returns to its languor.*

*Afterward, they pay a brief visit to the House of
Representatives. Not nearly so interesting. If the
Senate suffers from desuetude, the House is a scene
of utter chaos for the spectator. A minor bill in
mid-passage. Members rush down to the micro-
phones to praise or vilify it, each obliged to blurt
out his arguments in sixty seconds before the Speaker's gavel bangs him into silence. Then members*

55

converge on the center aisle where they march sheeplike between the tellers who solemnly pat each one's head to record his vote.

Here is mass democracy in action. For the life of him, B cannot comprehend how the members follow the noisy proceeding, much less act intelligently to affect its outcome. Mann assures him that rarely does anything happen in the chamber itself. Strategies are shaped and coalitions formed outside. Usually a dozen or so patriarchs determine the course of events. It is better this way, Mann argues. He has been present in the House on one or two occasions when the careful arrangements broke down and democracy really ruled. "It was a terrifying experience," says Mann.

Though I did not realize it fully at the time, a great war over Far East policy was brewing in Washington during my first winter. Get in or get out of Asia was the issue. The early skirmishes were waged along the corridors of the bureaucracy and in the secret recesses of the White House. But we received regular and full battle reports from Columnist Mann. He indicated that some policymakers were trying to find ways of making a 180-degree turnaround while pretending to go full steam ahead. Official rhetoric admitted nothing. But in the nooks and crannies of government men were talking; happy men who welcomed a policy shift and bitter men who wanted to sabotage it. The newspapers and news magazines carried premature post mortems describing in detail just who was doing what to whom.

Mann, a resplendent little man, thumbs cocked in his double-breasted waistcoat, gave the Dana guests a blow-by-blow account of the inside drama in which some men were heroes and others knaves. They were remarkably indiscreet in showing him policy papers, intelligence reports, and other literature stamped with the seal of national security. His columns were full of learned references to these documents, along with hints that there was even more to be revealed if the going got rough. For Mann had freely offered himself as a mercenary in the combat. Other columnists were lining up on the opposite side, fed a similar flow of intelligence data by their "inside" sources.

I formed a curious impression of Mann during these encounters. He seemed to revel in the conflict even though he was so firmly committed to one side. The issues were admittedly grave and, given the occasion, he affected long-jawed solemnity in prognosticating dire consequences for our nation. Still I couldn't take him altogether at face value. Was it that he showed too much joy of combat? Too much craving for controversy? I had the feeling that he, too, wore a mask.

Mann's poses could be outrageous at times. "Utter asses," he trumpeted one evening. "Utter asses who pretend to be policymakers." He went on to castigate his adversaries about real or imagined wrongs they had perpetrated. Dana, appearing unusually pensive, chided Mann for giving the policy fight a "clarity" that was misleading. He came near to dipping into his own experience by denying that these tidy press stories could convey the real reality. "It is a remarkable fact," Dana argued, "how men's memories can differ twenty-four hours after an event. Who influenced whom at the conference table? What motivated one participant to speak up and another to subside?"

Mann replied that he had always been able to rely on a particular policymaker for a good account. Dana agreed acidly that this policymaker had a remarkably vivid memory because he always viewed what was happening through the narrow blinders of his colossal ego. "His only trouble is that he isn't the one who makes the final decision. It is the President who decides and he is being buffeted by pressures and persuasions that lie completely beyond your informant's reckoning."

Long afterward, I tried to detect a meaning in Dana's outburst. He had been present many times at the conference table when weary men wrestled with intractable problems and slowly edged toward new policies. But all he seemed to suggest was that the heart of this process is unknowable; that decision-making in the government must remain a mystery incapable of either prediction or post mortem.

That same evening, according to my notebook entry, the tranquility of the Dana salon was rudely disturbed:

A real cat-and-dog fight between two members of the Senate. All during the dinner hour they keep itching for it and finally when the men are alone, it breaks out in full fury. Senator Todd triggers it by asserting he has reached the conclusion that the U.S. hasn't any business getting involved in affairs outside our country since all we manage to do is support the corrupt and the reactionary.

Is that so, retorts Senator Cox, then how come

58

we've managed to keep the Communists from tak-
ing over a large part of the earth's land mass when
this was plainly their ambition?

Senator Todd says he refuses to be impressed
every time somebody hollers Communist. So what
if the Communists do take over these corrupt little
countries? No reason to think they would be any
worse off than they are now.

Senator Cox expresses amazement at Senator
Todd's failure to learn anything from history. If it
teaches anything, history teaches that you don't get
anywhere by appeasing totalitarian powers.

Things are getting heated, but nobody has the
heart to intervene. Senator Todd, seeing there are
not many points to be scored debating history,
switches to the domestic arena. He is damned tired
of pumping money and men's lives down the rat-
holes abroad when there are so many things at home
that need doing. It is damned frustrating the way
the military men can get every last dollar they ask
for while domestic programs suffer each new bud-
get squeeze.

By now, Senator Todd has a full head of steam.
With the zeal of an old-time evangelist, he conducts
a tour d'horizon of our domestic woes, cataloguing
each one in loving detail. He is bound to conclude,
he ends mournfully, that a system is sick which al-
lows such evils to continue.

Old Cox appears to be going down for the ten
count. Doggedly, he seeks to regain the initiative.
Just how does Todd propose to organize power so

59

as to achieve his noble objectives? Is there another system of government practiced by man that could bring the millennium at a faster clip? When Todd answers rather sulkily that the way to begin is to begin, Cox delivers the low blow he has been preparing all evening. Perhaps, he says with an appearance of sweet reasonableness, Todd will join him in the first step by co-sponsoring a bill to purge the nation of domestic violence through rigid gun controls? As Cox well knows, Todd will do nothing of the sort since he comes from a Western state where guns stand second only to motherhood in the public sentiment.

Dana, sensing that his party is getting rough, finds a graceful way to break it up. Rising to join the ladies, he says he is reminded of the old Texan who, when asked his opinion on an issue, responded, "I ain't decided which side I'm on, but when I do, I'm prepared to be damned bitter."

B is impressed—and not a little depressed—by the fundamental split between these two members of the nation's great deliberative assembly. But when he remarks later on this, Dana snorts: "They are professional wrestlers, each struggling to get a toehold on the other, with loud grunts and groans and a great deal of thrashing about. They could swap roles and never know the difference. Neither one will ever lead a revolution—or a counter-revolution. These are not serious men."

"These are not serious men." It was a judgment that in one form or another Dana passed on a good many men

60

during my stay with him. Usually he did it less solemnly, often with the flash of wit for which he was known. But it was always the same judgment. I began to perceive that Dana, beneath his surface calm, was himself an intensely serious man. He believed that great issues were at stake in Washington, believed this so deeply that he would not engage in the mock debates staged by Mann and the rest. And I came later to learn that Dana had become a deeply pessimistic man.

VII

Lady M at dinner this evening. Promptly after-ward B hastens to get on paper a rough sketch of the formidable woman. A triumph to lure Lady M outside her own genteelly shabby salon to which in-vitations are widely sought and sparingly issued. B has heard of Lady M's reputation long before com-ing to Washington. Once he watched on television as this octagenarian bearded and bested a panel of in-terviewers. Spinster daughter of a long-ago Speaker of the House, she has become an institution in the nation's capital. Rather she has become an oracle whose utterances keep politicians in a state of ter-ror.

Close up, Lady M, whose title to ladyship is pure journalistic invention, presents a contrast to every-thing B anticipated. Lean, lithe grace of a woman many years her junior. Her face, in repose, gives

62

away her age, but her face is seldom in repose. It is a kaleidoscope of merriment, mock anger, gentleness, severity, irony, adulation. Networks of tiny lines appear and disappear like little coveys of birds. Only eyes remain constant, large blue-green eyes that penetrate a man.

How can this gentle old woman be the scourge she is known to be? Then while the eyes still twinkle and the birdlike voice prattles on, the rapier flashes and an admiring bystander suddenly gasps. Wit and irreverence tumble out helter-skelter. She seems to have no battle plan in her verbal forays yet there is not the faintest hint that senility has set in. Midflight she can halt a thrust when she detects that enough have hit home. Her face and voice combine to make an art of caricature, her strong chin being capable of receding into slack-jawed occlusion to imitate her victim. The waspish voice hardens into a nasal twang when she undertakes to mimic President Harding's wife, an intimate of former years. One could believe that Harding's uncouth "Duchess" had come back to life so that she might extol the virtues of her "Wurr'n" to the Dana guests.

B is amused that the men present do not seem entirely at ease with Lady M. He begins to see why when one Senator gets in her sights, a tiresome young fuddy-duddy who last week proposed with great fanfare that the President make a walking tour of the ghettos. Now Lady M suggests sweetly that since the Senator's committee deals with ocean-

63

*ography he ought to spend a portion of his time ex-
ploring sea bottoms. Young fuddy-duddy is not
amused.*

*The point of Lady M's wit is that she has no
credo that she wishes to impose on those who gov-
ern. Out of her long past, she has evolved the firm
notion that politicians need to keep a sense of pro-
portion about their place in the scheme of things.
She abhors their preoccupation with pinning the
label of "greatness" on one another. No one can be
judged great, Lady M maintains, until he is fifty
years mouldering in the grave. She is happy to go
about her self-appointed task of deflating those who
seek to rush history's verdict.*

*When no one else is listening, B attempts to probe
her thoughts on Chester Dana. She fixes him with a
merry eye. "Young man, I have always refused to
conspire in the sordid business of biography, even
my own." Then, as B looks crestfallen, she adds
"Dana is a man with almost female intuitions. A
long time ago he taught himself to lock them up inside. He is a good man, a tragic man. There, now,
Mr. Bohun, you've got more than you bargained
for."*

VIII

I TRAVELED the hundred miles south to Richmond during that first winter pressed by a strong urge to make a search in Dana's boyhood territory. During the journey, I remember sorting my impressions of what I would find. They consisted of very few hard facts. Most were the feelings of a Southerner who was not, as they say, "well born" toward a Southerner who was.

My first rude shock came on approaching the ancestral mansion which, in my mind's eye, still stood dominant and splendid at the long lane's end—a sort of Tara revisited. This was Tara, all right, but more like the home Scarlett O'Hara came back to when the Civil War was over. No war had ravaged the Dana birthplace, merely the forces of urban blight. Where once had been green lawns there was now a maze of shabby little houses. Rising close to the Dana mansion stood an ugly tenement, its walls facaded with imitation-brick asbestos. The mansion itself retained traces of its former elegance, large, stately, but with paint peeling on the spacious veranda and in one of the front

65

windows the awful hand-lettered sign ROOMS FOR RENT.

A sullen young man, his pallor accentuated by a day's growth of beard, admitted me to the front parlor and then, with considerable skepticism, allowed a tour of the house. He had not heard of Dana nor cared that this had been his birthplace. "It belongs to my mama now, but everything's so run-down that she's fixing to get shut of it," he said in a tone, half-whine, half-resignation. They had heard rumors that "niggers" were going to be moving into the neighborhood. He gave a sickly, yellow-toothed grin as if to share with me a common pride in our lily-white ancestry. "When that happens, we sure will git out in a hurry. Guess we'll have to head back to the country." As I peered into one dismal mildewed room after another, a brood of barefoot children, still in their nightclothes, peeped from behind the doorways and broke into noisy laughter every time I tried to catch a glimpse of them. I remember the oniony smell of dirty socks. In a bedroom upstairs, shades drawn, Mama still lay abed, not bothering to look up as we passed by. Probably she thought that I was a prospective boarder.

I tried my best, eyes half-closed, to shut out the squalor and call up images of a happier time when the home was storehouse for all the pleasures and pains of Chester Dana's growing up. But the effort was too much. Time's deforming hand had obliterated the past, leaving only a mockery of the earlier splendor. Had young Dana, with his prescience, sensed the ravages that lay ahead? Was this the reason he departed his birthplace, abandoned the family ties to the South, made his career up North?

Much later, when I had fitted together other pieces of the family puzzle, this supposition did not seem farfetched. The

66

Danas were, indeed, of a long line stretching back into Virginia's aristocracy. But the line was growing thin even before Chester Dana was born. Much had been expected of Stephen Dana, his father, who was the only son of an only son. And Stephen, taking a wife at an early age, had sired two sons. That had been the only productive thing he did. He flouted the family's tradition in the ministry and the law, choosing instead to live on his inheritance. He learned all too well the tradition of alcoholic excess nurtured by the young aristocrats at the University of Virginia. He departed Charlottesville without a degree, married a professor's pretty daughter, and settled into the old family homestead. Stephen Dana, whose photographs show a handsome young man with a gleam in the eye, soon became a solitary world wanderer. In Chester's ninth year, word reached the household that his father had died while touring the south of France. Anxious friends had pried as best they could but no word of explanation ever escaped the family's lips. The family finances had not stood the strain. Shortly before Chester departed for Harvard, his mother sold off a large portion of the Dana land and later disposed of the house itself, finishing her days in a small apartment in downtown Richmond. A fragile woman of deep emotions, she lived only a short time beyond Chester's wedding day.

What a contrast to the existence I had imagined—this sad, silent erosion of fortune and status. What contrast to my own growing up in a family which, not having had anything to lose, could inspire its heir with the brash optimism that there was everything to gain. Around my father's house no ancestors peered from the walls in dark oiled disapproval, no antique hand-me-downs suggested that the Bohuns had once been people of culture and substance. We lived close to the bone and my father worked a six day week even as his father and his father's father. At some distant point in time, Bohun farmers had retreated from small worn-out land holdings to take up clerical careers in the towns of southside Virginia. None had ever distinguished himself for good or evil. Only I, David Bohun, by some mysterious blending of the blood, was able to escape this rut and seek my way in a world where men get paid for employing their brains to do something other than tot up figures.

There are advantages in being the bright child in a long line of dullards. From an early age, I was the special light in my mother's eye, the means of breaking away from the humdrum existence that kept her forever in thrall. For my father, too, there was pride in a precocious son who could use big words and put them on paper for others to read. Neither minded that my verbal dexterity was accompanied by an uncommon amount of soul-searching and occasional outbursts of resentment that fate had launched me from such ordinary beginnings. Even my defiance of Southern mores, announced unctuously during one summer's leave from Harvard, provoked only minor consternation. My mother assured me that she read the same Bible and prayed to the same God of justice that she hoped I still prayed to. But it wouldn't help my father's job security for me to carry my racial views around town on a banner. And that was the end of that as far as they were concerned.

The point is that I grew up in a home where great and unusual things were expected of me. Among neighbors, I was the bright Bohun boy who won the insurance company's essay contest and got himself a scholarship to go way up North to college. A few snickered behind my back and a few more wondered out loud if I hadn't grown too big for my britches. But when I came home for visits and my dad took me downtown and introduced me to every living soul there, most of them always said how "proud" they were of my success.

"Mr. Turnipseed, you remember my boy, David, who's off at Harvard?"

"I sure do remember David. He's grown up to be a mighty fine young man. You not married yet, are you son?"

"No sir, Mr. Turnipseed, but I'm getting it pretty regular up at Harvard."

"Well son, we sure are proud of what you're doing. I know your mother must be proud of you. Your dad here, you only have to look at him to know how proud he is."

"I'm pretty proud of me, too, Mr. Turnipseed."

Of course, I never yielded to these fantasies but gave the dutiful response and stood silently while my father picked up conversation grown dog-eared with habit. They never seemed to mind or even to notice that I had become a total stranger in their midst, though I once overheard a family friend complain mildly, "For such a bright boy, he sure does keep most of it to himself."

But what meant most to me was I grew up knowing I was different. As far back as I can remember, I knew it but the real turning point came at ten when I spent the better part of a year recuperating from a bout of polio. It closed the door to a good many pursuits of boyhood, but I never missed them at all, for it opened the door to the secret world of imagining where I am destined to spend most of my life. It left only slight physical traces, an irregularity in the rhythm of the hips which I counterbalance by standing very straight and walking very stiff. I wear a lift under my right heel, and become acutely conscious of my deformity in moments of sexual enterprise which require me to take off my clothes. But the gain from polio far outweighed the loss, or at least I have believed this to be so for it confirmed my difference and liberated me. It produced a feeling that I had been "mercifully blessed" to have survived the scourge with no more crippling effect. Many a conversation in the front parlor of our small house took the familiar litany.

"David is a mighty lucky young man, Mrs. Bohun, not to be spending his life in an iron lung like some people we know."

"I can tell you, Mrs. Turnipseed, that we prayed over that boy. The Lord answered our prayers."

We did pray over me. I remember at ten years of age praying with all the passion I could muster while the dread fever burned high and the ache racked my bones. Afterward, I strove mightily to pay back the Lord by my devotion. In the drear old church where my family practiced its fundamentalist faith, I was a regular communicant. Each Sunday morning and more often when the visiting evangelist came to town, I joined in shouting the lusty hymns, full of the blood of the Lamb and other vivid metaphor. With bowed head and bent knee, I followed the free-flowing prayers to God, admiring the rhetoric delivered with such verve and gusto by the unschooled church elders. I sat with abiding patience while the preacher hammered home his message about the Hope of Heaven and the Fear of Hell, always ending up with the passionate appeal for sinners to come forward and be saved. Then one Sunday I, too, went forward and afterward braved the icy waters of the baptismal tank. Before the sweetly singing congregation, gently cradled in the preacher's arms, I was buried in Christ and rose again, wet, bedraggled, saved.

Religion, like so many other heritages from this Southern community, has left only a slight residue after my purgative years at Harvard. But still a residue remains. Even now it provokes the spasms of self-doubt, the agonies of indecision as I seek my true identity. Will the real David Bohun please stand up? No single soul could answer that call because there is no real David Bohun. He is an amalgam, fused into one crippled body, of youthful soul-saver, pretentious scholar, facile word-slinger, and now tormented pilgrim into the life and times of Chester Dana.

I turned Richmond upside down seeking for the residue of Dana's boyhood. At what point in time did he come to recognize that he was marked for a separate destiny? The bits and pieces I managed to pick up offered meager gleanings. By all reports, he was "extremely close" to his widowed mother, a dutiful elder son, obedient and good to a woman who was often ridden with sickness and emotion. The Dana family nursed their tragedy to themselves and maintained only the barest ties to more fortunate relatives. Chester and his brother attended the Barnham School for Boys where, the school management being hard pressed for tuitions, the "best" boys of Richmond consorted with the worst dropouts from the public school system. One former inmate, a dapperly dressed shoe salesman in one of Richmond's leading department stores, recalled for me that he himself had been one of the delinquents. He described with relish what daily hell they raised despite the headmaster's efforts to preserve a standard of excellence. But Dana had never been a hell-raiser. He was a good boy, held in faint awe by his contemporaries, privately derided by some as a mama's darling. Diligent in his studies, he was also more than competent in athletics. But, all in all, he was a loner.

I visited the decrepit two-story brick building, since turned into a motorboat emporium, where Chester Dana pursued his studies along with sixty other Barnhamites. The main assembly hall had been altered, its walls knocked out to make way for storefront windows. But the musty upstairs classrooms remained unchanged, blackboards intact, row on row of spread-arm desks provoking an image of grubby boys hard at the task of growing up. Down in the dim-lit basement, the dank stall of urinals roused other images of youths swapping sex lore, dreaming their first misshapen fantasies about the coming conquest of womankind. Did Dana ever dream such dreams?

The emporium's owner, by good chance, was a Barnham alumnus and a Dana classmate. His memory had grown misty after so many years in motorboats but, with cajoling, he finally recalled an episode that occurred, believe it or not, in the stench of the dismal basement lavatory. There, during recess period, a fifteen-year-old exhibitionist named Longstreet was treating three or four of the younger boys to their first lesson in sex play, fly open, fist actively at work, when Dana chanced to come upon the bug-eyed group. "Longstreet, what do you think you are doing?" The simplicity of Dana's query had not concealed its severity. This promptly broke up the budding orgy and became a part of

72

Barnham legend. It still lived fresh in the emporium owner's failing memory. He recollected that Longstreet had gone on to follow his father's career in the ministry but, whether from sexual excess or other causes, had long since departed this earthly life.

I found the revelation uncommonly fascinating, for I had received my early coaching in sex from a contemporary who was the preacher's son across the street. Curiosity had kept me from turning it aside in Dana's fashion. What a fount of misinformation was my tutor! He was right on the basic role of the genitalia, but described a gruesome climax in which a single drop of male urine became within the female a quart of baby's blood. My primer lesson in the miracle of human reproduction left such repulsion that for a long time I could not behold parent, preacher, or other childbearing adults without wondering how they ever brought themselves to indulge in this depravity.

But if Dana brooded about these matters or was repulsed by the lust that gave him birth, there was no way of digging it out of the silent Richmond past. He, along with his mother and brother, was a churchgoer at Epiphany Episcopal, a stately cathedral still frequented by the city's first families. I worshiped there one Sunday simply to get the feel of the place, contrasting its elegant rituals with the stark ones of my own bygone faith. A mighty church organ sent forth hymns to God, setting loose echoes that made it well-nigh impossible for human voices to chime in. Instead of the amateur prayers delivered by church elders that I remembered, we accompanied the clergy in recitals from the prayer book. In place of the leather-lunged, blue-serge-

73

suited preacher of my youth, a cultivated pastor wearing full clerical garb spoke to us in an accent heavy with the broad *a*s and soft *u*s of tidewater Virginia.

Here was a place where a youth could approach God in a dignified, verily a dispassionate, manner. I doubted that Epiphany Episcopal had ever provoked in Dana the torment of soul that I had known. His must have been a more controlled religiosity, well defined in its spiritual demands, offering an appropriate reward not merely in life hereafter but in earthly status as well. Even as I write, I feel the prejudices of the fundamentalist toward the high churcher. So many rigid attitudes shaped by my harsh faith remain even after faith has long since lost its fierce grip on me. We believed that the Lord forbade instrumental music in His House. We believed that baptism was to be consummated by total immersion, not by the sprinkling of a few drops of water. We read the Good Book and took as a firm article of faith that every Sunday, not simply once a month, we must break the bread and drink the wine of Holy Communion. Finally, we believed that Christ had lived and died to make each man his own priest, nowhere providing for a hierarchy of bishops and other potentates. And believing all this, we developed stern feelings toward those who pursued less strict religions. And yet, and yet. I am aware that Dana's discreet relationship to God lasted him over a lifetime, while my ties were loosed with the first buffeting. Dana kept up his church attendance at the Washington Cathedral, even when he was discarding other faiths.

One final fragment of my notes on the sojourn in Richmond gives insight into the boyhood of Chester Dana. Quite by accident, for neither Dana nor his wife had volunteered the information, I discovered that brother Paul, his junior by three years, was still alive and residing in a nursing home on the outskirts of the city. We spent a long afternoon together strolling around the manicured lawns of this domicile, quite obviously the final gathering place for wealthy incurables. Paul Dana, whose ailment was discreetly referred to as chronic intestinal disorder, had been an inmate for quite some time—financed, I learned later, by his older brother.

Their blood linkage was evident at first glance, but so were the startling differences that time had worked on the two men. Paul seemed many years the senior, gaunt, stooped, both in mien and bearing robbed of the vitality that his brother displayed. He had the handsome Dana brow and nose, only on a shrunken scale giving an appearance of weakness in contrast to Chester's strength. His hair was snow-white, not iron-gray.

But the more shocking contrast was in the younger Dana's manner. Life had been hard on him and he spared me no detail. He was a chain smoker. Speaking in a voice grown thin with the combined assaults of illness and cigarettes, Paul Dana was an habitual whiner about the fate that thrust him down while his brother moved ever upward.

They had, I gathered, never been close. While still a boy, Paul was afflicted with rheumatic fever that weakened his heart. It made him the object of his mother's pampering and, I gathered, her favoritism. Had Chester ever suffered bad health? "No," Paul's reply scarcely concealed a bitter note, "the good Lord always blessed Chester with a strong constitution." Soon after their father's death, Chester did have a severe attack of what appeared to be asthma. But it

75

passed. So far as Paul knew it was the first and last time Chester was really sick.

It became clear that Paul knew precious little about his brother. Recurrent invalidism had not helped to deepen or sweeten Paul's spirit but instead turned him in on himself. He had somehow made his way through preparatory school, probably because of Barnham's desperate need for tuition payments. But his career at the University of Virginia was short-lived; his problem, like his father's, being a greater propensity for the bottle than the books. After that, he made one serious effort at private enterprise, a portion of the family funds being used to purchase the franchise for an automobile agency. Fate once again played him tricks and Paul lost control of the agency, preserving in the bargain lifetime rights to continue as a commissioned salesman.

Life in a Southern town can be cruel, but it has always offered a crutch for ne'er-do-well sons of fine old families. Back home, I knew many like Paul Dana who just barely managed to make a go of it with frequent boosts and occasional outright charity from a community resigned to the fact that every litter must have its runt. I have wondered what ill allocation of the genes causes one child, like Chester Dana, to go forth with a giant's capacity while a second, like Paul, bearing the selfsame heritage, commences to shrivel almost on leaving his mother's womb. Or does environment make the dreadful difference? Could the blow dealt by a father's untimely death harden one son in his resolve to get ahead while it crippled the other?

Driving back from Richmond, I brooded over these mysteries. My brief encounter with Dana's childhood—with the rise and fall of a venerable family—had produced in me a deep melancholy. This was the last of the line. Paul had never married; Chester had no surviving son. The resurgence of energy and ambition that produced Chester's spectacular career was now spent. When he died there would be little left to remember. One thing I had clearly learned during my journey south: I learned why Chester Dana had left his heritage at the earliest opportunity and why, having left, he never looked back.

IX

March 7, A.D. 1

Scandal is in the air this spring leaving a fat pungent smell, slightly akin to a fart, that has everyone sniffing and looking nervously at his neighbor. Word of it is brought to the Dana salon by Mann who titillates us with the news that a high regulatory official, Howard Frost—"the old, old friend of the President"—is suspected of sexual "indiscretions." Worse yet, they reportedly occurred while he was being entertained by an industry he is supposed to regulate. Like most really juicy scandals, this one promises to leak out a few drips at a time. According to Mann, the press will give it a preview with tips supplied by an obliging committee counsel on Capitol Hill. Then Congress will move in once the victim has been exposed sufficiently to be sure he has no alibi.

78

Mann recounts all this to B in a state of high glee. For him, it is fodder for many righteous columns indicting the man, the system, and the state of public morality which allows such a thing to happen. Why did it happen, B demands of the all-knowing columnist? "The old Washington melodrama, my boy. The young lawyer comes to the capital, ambitious, full of piss and vinegar, determined to avoid a dry-dust career in private practice. Finds happiness here, works his way rung by rung up the bureaucratic ladder, begins to savor the sweetness when his word—his decision—can affect other men's fortunes. He has patience, persistence and the unbelievable good luck of having known the President when he was a nobody. So he reaches the regulatory commission where in return for low pay and long hours he can preside over the destiny of a vast industry. Then the slow descent begins. He gets tired of being eternally poor, especially while watching how lushly other men live. His furnace breaks down, his roof leaks, his son busts out of college. His wife, serene and sacrificing during the long upward journey, turns into a nagging bitch. He gets bitter. Why has the President left him to rot on this damned old commission? Why shouldn't a man enjoy the good things of life while he still has a little lead left in his pencil?"

B once met the portly Commissioner, jovial, large-jawed, only the tight lines around his eyes betraying internal stress. Now B wonders how long he has lived in terror of exposure. Mann, smug, cyni-

cal, sees a larger explanation for the scandal. "This town is full of men who would be obliged to head for the border if their private sins were exposed. But they don't get exposed, not unless someone has a larger aim in view. The poor old Commissioner happens to be the President's crony—or at least that's what he will be made out to be—and that's who they're gunning for."

Gossip in the Dana drawing room gnaws on this bone for all its worth. It divides the group, B observes, into two factions: the indignant and the philosophical. He tries to find each group's identifying traits. Of course, the women are united in their anger at this betrayal of the public's trust and, one suspects, the wife's hegemony over her husband's sex organ. But there are also indignants among the men, usually those with inherited wealth. Having grown contemptuous of the craving for money, they profess contempt for anyone who does not share their notions of self-sacrifice in public service. The other, philosophical group is composed mostly of those who made it the hard way like the poor Commissioner. They lapse into long silences, draw deeply on their cigars, and, by their diffidence, express "But for the grace of God, there go I."

Mann, not content to leave the subject alone, tries out ideas for a future column by baiting the men over their after-dinner coffee cups. "One could construct a picture of power in Washington simply by tracing a chart of who has who by the short hairs. It wouldn't make a very pretty picture. No one, not even the President himself, is immune from this exotic game of pull and tug. Everybody is exposed and the higher he climbs the fuller he exposes himself. I daresay it really contributes to the civility of things—a sort of domestic system of mutual deterrence."

He succeeds in stirring Dana's ire. "As usual, Henry, your metaphors are as faulty as your philosophy. Maybe it serves your circulation purposes to create this picture of sex athletics in the nation's capital. It may even gratify your readers to think of their leaders engaged in Olympian contests. But I doubt if it adds much to the sum of knowledge."

Mann, elated that he has provoked controversy, slides off the point by protesting that his metaphor has been misunderstood. "I do not speak solely of sex. All I mean to say is that each man has his vulnerability, or to put it less elegantly, each man can be 'got to.' It causes a splash when somebody gets caught diddling a tart. But my point is that everybody in high office has an equivalent sin. It's what makes him human, And, when you balance things out, it's what makes government responsive to the people."

Senator Vale, who has led many forays against corruption, hurrumphs angrily. "I cannot possibly see, Mr. Mann, how government is improved by the frailties you claim are so universal among the governors."

"My dear Senator," responds the columnist in a

81

state of excitement now that he is the center of attention, "how else do you overcome man's temptation to arrogance when he gets into a place of power? Humility is not a virtue that comes easily to men in public life. It must be acquired, usually by the fear that your secret shame will out. We have damned few Abraham Lincolns around. Even Lincoln, if we only knew, must have had an unmentionable private sin that made him so longsuffering."

Dana becomes rather impassioned. "Each of us sees Washington through his own prism. To be sure, the city has its share of lust, of corruption, of depravity. No more, perhaps, than any other city its size. But what doesn't come through your prism, Henry, are the ideals that also live here, often live in the same man who succumbs to temptations of the flesh. What makes a Hugo Black outgrow his regional prejudices and become a great Justice of the Supreme Court? What causes each President to be a better man than we have any right to expect of him? I say there is a morality that affects our government." Dana is breathing heavily, like a man whose emotions are stirred.

But Mann isn't letting go so easily. "And I say balls! What you call morality can be perfectly well explained as playing to a larger audience. Old Hugo Black was a Klansman when it served his needs to get elected in Alabama. He became a great constitutionalist when he had to perform for the audience that watches the Supreme Court. Our Presidents go

82

through the same transformation when they move to a bigger constituency. It all depends on who is watching whom."

Senator Vale appears weary of the argument. "By your lights, what prevents our government from heading into collapse?"

And Mann retorts: "Fear of exposure, by God, that is the main corrective. Fear of exposure."

By now, Lady M has returned to the room, always being impatient with the after-dinner separation of the sexes. Eyes a-twinkle, she moves in on Mann. "Surely, my dear Henry, that same corrective is what keeps all the rest of us in our pristine state—our journalistic brethren no less than others. Perhaps we should start a round-robin confession this evening. For a start, tell us what is the private sin that keeps you so uncorrupted?"

Mann, recognizing that he has met his match, mutters that his proposition applies only to those in power. It is a misstep which Lady M is quick to pursue. "But you can't possibly mean that you columnists have no power. Sometimes as I consume your morning produce, I fancy that you are the only ones who have undisputed power—the only ones really free from fear of exposure."

Again and again the rapier stabs until poor Mann, desperate to get loose, tries to change the subject with uncharacteristic crudity:

"Lady M, something I have always yearned for is to serve as pallbearer at your funeral. Do you think I can aspire to that honor?"

83

Once more the blue-green eyes of this pretty oc-togenarian begin to twinkle. She shows no fear of approaching death. "I'm afraid not, dear sweet Henry. You see, I have left firm instructions that I wish to be cremated. Would you like to sprinkle me?"

B is surprised to see that Chester Dana has with-drawn from the fray. While his guests prattle on, he sits morosely staring into the fire, thinking his own thoughts. Has he dismissed Mann's swiftly shaped theories as too contemptible for response? Or has Mann happened upon some personal truth in Dana's own life, touched a nerve that stirs remem-bered pain?

After the guests leave, B tries to probe this terri-tory by alluding to the earlier exchange. But he misses the mark. "Oh, that fellow," Dana answers with a dry laugh. "He has the persistence of a horse-fly. And he likes to feed on the same kind of offal." Then he adds almost affectionately, "But there's more to Mann than his ridiculous poses."

X

CORRUPTION held a fascination for me when I was young. Something about my upbringing in a religious faith which read each word of the New Testament for its literal meaning. I pondered Christ's admonition that even to look at a woman lustingly was a sin equal to adultery. What an impossible standard for a boy passing through puberty! By rough estimate, I calculated that I must have earned Hell's damnation at least ten thousand times in the spirit before earning it in the flesh.

My proximity to sin made me wonder what causes a man to grow corrupt. Was corruption a state of being or a state of mind? As a boy, I spent summer vacations with cousins whose stepfather served as warden on the state prison farm. There we would pass the afternoons listening to the trusties as they indulged in reminiscence. One memory has lingered: none was guilty. Not one, whether he had been convicted of robbing a bank or killing his mother-in-law, deserved the punishment being meted out to him. I used to

85

have nightmares about this endless parade of innocents through the penitentiary gates.

Perhaps this was why Commissioner Frost's predicament would not let go of me. I did not really know the man. But he seemed more my type than the Danas of this world. I was provoked to put myself in his shoes, share his torment, indulge in fantasy which I recorded in my notebook:

SOLILOQUY OF COMMISSIONER FROST

Washington is a cruel city. When you're up, everybody's with you. They smile and smile and a man can howdy-do himself to death, thinking how important he is. When you're down, they still smile and a few even pat you on the back. But everybody knows it's not the same.

I know because I've been guilty myself when others got hauled up like big fat river fish and left to suck air in the bottom of the boat. I used to tut-tut with the rest of them, all the while secretly enjoying how old John or Tom or Abe was getting his comeuppance. Don't fool yourself, mister. Everybody in this goddamn town enjoys a scandal no matter what kind of public face he puts on. I love to read these press fellows, squeezing the last drop of unction out of my predicament. Hell! If I hadn't given them something real to bellyache about, they would be making it up out of whole cloth. Talk about corruption, the godalmighty press in this town is so corrupt it doesn't know the meaning of that word.

Am I corrupt? I've given the worst years of my

life to this government because I thought it was a good and noble thing to do. I've stayed poor when I could have got rich, easy and safe. I've loved my wife—she'll never believe that now—even though she long ago quit loving me in the ways that count. Taking her to bed was like doing it to the mattress; only a mattress wouldn't pretend to be so longsuffering.

I feel like a big fat fish. Right now, all over town they're serving me on the menu and enjoying every morsel. Everybody's got his theory of why I did it. Some will be claiming they knew all along I was a wrong one—didn't like the way I combed my hair or picked my teeth. What they mean is that they can't stand the notion of a poor boy getting anywhere. Leave public office to the rich pricks, third generation, so they can pay for their own sins. It doesn't matter whether their granddaddies robbed the government blind in piling up that money. They've got style.

Some will claim they feel sorry for me. They blame the system. Shit. I blame the system, too, Fuck a system that makes you sit there day after day watching those greedy bastards fighting to get their share and expects you to find some "judicial" way of deciding among them. There ain't no way to decide. Flipping a coin would make just as much sense as what we had to do. Nothing in the holy writ of the Constitution can tell you whether company A or company B has the right to make a bundle on the public franchise. Despite all the mumbo-

87

jumbo we went through, we knew and they knew it was a load of crap. But how do you change the system? Somebody's got to decide and if you're Jesus H. Christ himself, it'll get you in the end.

A sweet favor the old man did by letting me be the one! The day he handed me this job he gave a pep talk about how his enemies would be gunning for me so as to destroy him. I believed him, so help me God, and I've turned down more bribes than he'll ever know. Big bribes offered me by big shots here in town who are now riding their righteous high horses along with the rest. Do you get any brownie points in Heaven for the sins you don't commit?

Am I corrupt? Every man has his itch. For some it's money and, Lord, what they'll do to get it. But I never really wanted money that much. They can pore over my bankbooks till Judgment Day and they won't learn any more than I can tell them right now, which is that yours truly is a poor man. Some men itch for the bottle like it was mother's milk. But my itch is the same one that pestered old Adam himself. And I can't help myself when once in a while that itch has got to be rubbed.

It was a damn fool thing to do. There are quieter places where a man can find a woman. That evening I hadn't meant to do more than drop by the party, pay my respects, and head home to the cold comfort of my Molly. But she was there, laughing loudest at my jokes, glancing sideways at me when the conversation ran down. Man, you could smell it in the air. I knew she wasn't a lady and that she didn't really want to show me the magazine article in her room down the long hotel corridor. But wild horses couldn't have held me back. I'd believe they put Spanish Fly in my drink except that my itch is too old, too familiar. When I was a boy, I'd try cold showers but they never worked. Something happens inside me. The blood in my brain gets full of fatty stuff. I can't think, I can't breathe.

It took such a little time and I didn't even go back to the party. It wasn't the first time or the last time. But it damn sure was the wrong time and I guess I'll spend the rest of my life thinking about that.

XI

WALKING was Dana's recreation. He pursued it determinedly, keeping a pace that left me, several decades his junior, short of breath and sore of limb. But I accompanied him as often as he invited me, for these hikes provided the occasions to get to know him. They also gave me a chance to observe the beauty which is so intimate to Washington.

Tall, ramrod-straight, he habitually wore on these walks an old suede hunting jacket, plaid wool hat, knitted gloves, and swung a gnarled oak cane. His favorite route was up the towpath bordering the old C & O Canal which had been built to serve as a major channel of commerce in the nation's infant years. Now the canal lay idle except for the summer tourist barges run by the Park Service. The towpath, rising very gradually toward the mountains, served both hikers and cyclists. Later on, I was to learn that it also served lovers.

Dana followed the canal all year round. But he liked it best in the dead of winter. "I have always fancied seasons," he once told me, "but my taste has changed quite markedly over the years. Once I thought the whole world existed for springtime. Even during the worst periods of the war I used to slip away on a fine spring Sunday and pay court to the budding trees along this path all the way to Glen Echo and beyond. Gradually, I came to have a partiality for autumn. Not even New England can produce a finer riot of crimsons. I liked fall's constancy. Day after day of golden sunshine. Now I have turned to winter and its infinite shades of gray."

We had stopped at a clearing in the trees where a network of tiny frozen finger lakes stretched toward the Potomac River just beyond. The setting sun gave a silvery sheen to the somber landscape of Virginia shoreline and created a black web of tree reflections in the waters. Dana stood motionless, lost in musings. Then, finally: "It may be a part of growing old, but I like winter best of all. Its beauty is so serene."

These walking soliloquies were not melancholy. He did not speak of death and I never felt he feared the thought of dying. He was a disciplined observer and could describe in detail the flora and fauna of the territory we visited. A long time later, as I will record, he gave me further details about the C & O Canal, about George Washington's vision for this now-defunct channel of commerce. It had a meaning for the Dana story that I had never anticipated during those winter walks.

We followed other paths. We explored Rock Creek Park, the wilderness that threads its way right to the heart of the nation's capital. We hiked out to the end of Hains Point and watched the city's water traffic alternating with its aerial commerce. We visited the grave of Henry Adams' wife in

Rock Creek Cemetery and studied the statue created by Augustus Saint-Gaudens in memory of that tragic woman.

And almost always on our Sunday-afternoon expeditions we ended at the vesper service of the Washington Cathedral which broods high over the capital city. Dana said he much preferred the twilight to the morning for religious meditation. Sitting alongside him in that vaulting amphitheater, listening to the mighty organ chords ricochet from one stone battlement to the next, watching the dying sun fire the stained glass with ever deeper crimsons, I found myself losing my fundamentalist hostility toward the high church. I found pleasure in the echo and re-echo of readings from the Book of Prayer. For brief moments, I began to share with Dana the solace of his less demanding religion.

One weekday afternoon I accompanied Dana to the National Archives in search of a rare book which was stirring his interest at the time. Afterward, we stood before the display case containing the original manuscript of our nation's Constitution. "It started with these pieces of paper," he commented, "the problems as well as the promise. Such an idealistic document, setting forth precise principles for achieving a 'more perfect' union. 'To secure the blessings of liberty to ourselves and our posterity.' Yet, so cynical in counting the black as three-fifths a man. It began a compromise with principle that has dogged us till this day and will go on dogging us."

Afterward, we walked the few blocks to the heart of a black ghetto. A noisy swarm of children were playing kick-the-can amid the passing traffic. "Here we see the sordid side of our Constitution," Dana said. "If the Negro had fully counted and freely voted, this need not have happened. Congress would never have been allowed to subsidize landowners to curtail their crops and export their blacks to the cities instead. It was a catastrophe that far-sighted politics could have avoided."

On our travels, we often visited the museums of Washington. Dana loved most of all the National Gallery of Art bequeathed by Andrew Mellon. "This building is as much a masterpiece as any of the paintings hanging in it," he told me. "It is the appropriate way to appreciate art. Uncrowded and uncluttered." An unhurried man could spend an entire afternoon in a single gallery and Dana sometimes did. I began my education in art with him and soon discovered that we had a marked difference of taste. For reasons not entirely clear to me, I leaned strongly to the passionate oils of El Greco. I felt soul-sympathy for the powerful portrait of Saint Jerome, his body bared to the elements, his face revealing the ascetic's tortured yearning for some sign of God's inspiration. I found myself deeply moved by Saint Martin, obviously torn by conflicting feelings of love and selfishness as he shared his cloak with the beggar.

But Dana preferred less passionate painting. He had a liking, he told me, for the British school of the eighteenth century—Gainsborough, Constable, George Romney, Sir Joshua Reynolds. These were quiet, orderly works, both the landscapes and the great portraits of lovely ladies. One by Sir Henry Raeburn seemed particularly to catch his eye. It was a study in browns and beiges of a blonde woman, soft with dark eyes, posed against a misty outdoor setting. As I watched Dana watching her, I could not help making perverse comparison between this young woman and Dame Dana. Was she a reminder of the blonde from college days?

93

Was there another soft woman in Dana's life? Or was she the object of pure fantasy?

I became convinced of it during that long first winter: Dana was playing games with me. Dana was performing a biographical strip-tease, dropping one veil at a time. It was maddening the way this man could talk and talk and still conceal. I was reminded of an earlier writer's efforts to get at Bernard Baruch which ended in the bitter lament, "Baruch, squid-like, envelops himself in a dark cloud of self-revelation. The more he talks about himself, the more he obscures himself."

Dana's habit of concealment took a somewhat different form. He was clear, incisive, informed about the details of all the great matters of public policy which occupied his lifetime. He made witty, often acid-limned characterizations of other men who shared his occupation. But always there was the cool detachment, the sense of personal withdrawal. Often after a session of relentless probing, I came away knowing everything about the issue in question but sadly aware that I knew nothing about the blood-and-guts involvement of Chester Dana himself. When I pressed, an inner lid seemed to drop down over those ice-gray eyes and the old man turned aside the question as though it had never been asked.

So I screwed up my courage and pursued my quest. Carefully planning this foray ahead of time, I put to Dana a long series of hypothetical conclusions designed to draw him from his lair. They had to do, I remember, with the struggles of conscience that may occur for one who serves in an advisory role to the President. "How does an adviser strike a balance between conscience and effectiveness?" I

94

asked. Then I leaned back triumphantly to await the revelation. But no response was forthcoming. The seconds
ticked by and turned into minutes as I realized, slowly and
uncomfortably, that Dana had no intention of replying. For
what seemed like hours, the two of us conducted this silent
Indian wrestle. Then I broke first and falteringly moved on
to another topic.

Was this the passion for anonymity with which Presidential advisers are supposed to be imbued? Or did Dana's reticence come from bitter experience which taught the old
man never to offer too freely of himself?

That winter I began to feel like one of those hapless
steers brought to market who bangs its head first to one
side then to the other of the cattle chute as it advances to
its slaughter. It was interesting, I see in hindsight, that my
subconscious seized on the image of a steer. Why not a bull
or a heifer? There must be a sexual meaning in this, for I
was, in fact, beginning to doubt my own creative powers.
Maybe the fault was not Dana's at all. Why should an old
man, contemplating a lifetime of success, wish to be
plumbed and prodded to serve my purpose? Our unwritten
contract called for a straight biography—no more, no less.
If Dana had known my deeper design, he would have been
justified in turning me out of bed and board forthwith, as
an ingrate who accepts a man's hospitality and then takes
liberties with a man's life. A crime more flagrant than taking liberties with a man's wife—or his daughter.

My great distress was not caused by this deception, but
by the growing, gnawing doubt that I could perform my
self-assigned mission. There is a difference between probing
a figure already safely embalmed in the history books and a

95

man who still lives and breathes and puts on his shoes each morning. Historical research offers fair game for intellectual dilettantes. By flushing out a few fresh facts, one can construct entire new theories about the distant past and be widely acclaimed by one's fellow dilettantes. But writing about the living, I was discovering, is a different matter.

I have read the contemporary historian who deals confidently with living figures. He puts direct quotations in the President's mouth on occasions when no one could possibly have been present to record them. More annoying still, the historian describes precisely what prompted the President to take each major decision. His book becomes a bestseller, for readers want to know these things without ifs and buts. I am awed by the historian's mastery of his material, even more by his imaginative powers. For I cannot find such mastery or imagination within myself. As I attempt to reconstruct a single episode in Dana's career, I have been overwhelmed by a dozen different perspectives, a hundred conflicting facts, a myriad of possible motivations. Each bystander has his own interpretation of what caused an event to happen the way it did. I am convinced that a whole book could be written simply about why a man does a certain deed on a certain day.

The more I got past my beginning explorations into Dana's life the more I was obsessed with my subject. It became a testing of myself. Could I penetrate this man? Could I understand the mystery: Why at the prime of his career as adviser to the President did he break with the President? Why did he withdraw so abruptly and finally from public life? These questions had to be faced. I knew enough at this point to be certain that there was not a tidy explanation. I suspected that the reasons had not developed overnight.

Yet, living so close to my subject, I found that my artistry was crippled. I could not make the leaps of imagination that would impose a design on Dana's life. I could not even begin in an orderly way with the thousand brush strokes of detail leading toward the final portrait.

Those were awful days and they got worse as time went on. I had a panicky sense of weeks and months passing while I moved no nearer to the completion of my work. I found it difficult to set routines for myself, to fix a daily quota of words on paper which would give a feeling of progress. I remember trying all sorts of tricks to coax myself onward in my labors. I fashioned make-work projects to create the illusion of business. I spent vast amounts of time sharpening my pencils, straightening the yellow pads in a neat pile, gazing out the window of my tiny workroom in the Dana gatehouse, going to the bathroom, pouring a fresh cup of coffee, leafing through my notes—doing anything and everything, in fact, but move ahead on the biography.

In my frustration, I often made comparisons with others in Washington who earn their living in the word business. I counted the output of the syndicated columnist and marveled at his veritable torrent of prose, so olympian in tone, so purposeful in assembling bits and pieces from the universe and weaving them into a daily treatise. In a week's time, the columnist has passed life-and-death judgments on a score of men in public life while poor Bohun was faltering before a single one.

I envied—and still do—the rhythm of the editorial writers who serve the politicians their morning fare. How refreshing to rise each day with the germ of an idea tickling the brain, massage it through the morning and then, by mid-afternoon, clear one's system. I found myself more and more comparing the cerebral to the bodily functions. I have concluded there is something essentially unhealthy about writing books, for it fits no decent rhythm of life. Too long a stretch between the early urge and the final satisfaction. Too many opportunities for one's purpose to wilt, leaving one incapable of the sustained thrust needed to consummate the act.

As I contemplated the word-making industry of Washington, I decided that this city is not a proper environment for anyone engaged in a labor like mine. Here, words are articles of commerce, not the raw materials of art. Each day the traffic in words begins on the great trunk lines of the AP and UPI, words are cranked out by the silent steno-typists at the countless committee hearings, words are rushed into print for messages, speeches, reports. The President manufactures several tens of thousands of words in an ordinary week; lesser politicians are not far behind.

This leads the city to an irreverent attitude toward the production of books. A Senator calculates that it will assist his career to become an author so he hires one or two "helpers" and, lo, he is one. One of my reporter friends told me proudly of sitting at his desk one day when a publisher's agent phoned. "How about a book?" the agent asked. "What about?" replied the reporter. "You name it," said the agent. So the reporter picked his topic and three weeks later, working after hours, delivered his finished manuscript.

Washington is a city that begins every conversation between friends or strangers with the blunt query "What do

98

you do?" This is a hard question to get round if you are a writer, for it leads inevitably to the follow-up: "What are you writing?" A man can conceal much idleness by the simple retort "I practice law." No need to go further. But the writer who is not really writing has no such escape.

The Danas never pressed, but one terrible winter's night an obnoxious middle-aged bitch decided to push me to the mat. She was a woman well known as the purveyor of gossip to several of the more voracious female columnists. She carried on her conversations without trace of a smile or hint of compassion. Her face remained immobile; only the lips showed a sign of life. She had a muleskinner's voice and she smoked cigars in public.

"Surely, Mr. Bohun, you can give us some clue to how you are handling our friend Dana?" I demurred, saying it was against my practice to develop theories at such an early stage. "But you must know whether he is hero or villain? Have you found his weak spots?" With Chester Dana sitting nearby, I writhed under her inquisition until Henry Mann rescued me with a discussion of his own work habits. By the time he had finished, the bitch had contemptuously turned her attention elsewhere.

As the months passed, I found it hard to go on justifying a project that stretched out so open-endedly. I felt desperately that I must cut it short, wind it up, get on to other chores. What misbegotten fate had decreed that I should become so entangled with this man Dana?

Fear of literary impotence produced a mounting sexual frustration. I simply could not keep my mind off women. Sitting at my desk, I daydreamed about them, indulging in such acts of lust and lechery that my sensibilities were

99

rubbed raw. On the street, I had only to glimpse a comely passerby before mentally disrobing her. I began to fear for my sanity, to fear even more that thought would give way to act in an unguarded moment. One of the Dana maids, a full-blown Portuguese, came daily to tidy up my quarters, dark, olive complexioned, her rolled-down stockings revealing an ample stretch of thigh when she stooped to make my bed. Only by the severest test of will power, eyes firmly fastened on book, mind cogitating the consequences of disgrace, could I keep from toppling her where she stood. Even so, her departure always left me to uncontrolled fantasies involving cavorts on the bed with this buxom one.

I used to wonder why I was so different from other men who make their way in the nation's capital. From what I have been able to observe, they all get up each morning, put on their trousers one leg at a time, and face the day with definite notions of what their schedules will include. Even those who succumb to temptations of the flesh appear to program it according to planned routines, most of them preferring to separate their working from their lusting time. For me, each day is a chaos that defies my every attempt at carving out order. I have no notion of how to divide my hours, and given the option would infinitely prefer morning as the time for lovemaking. More and more I seem to move by fits and starts, screwing up my resolution, then lunging at each appointed task until I fall back exhausted. I doubt that these alternating periods of idleness and frenzy are the best way to spend my energies. But I am incapable of doing it any other way.

Chester Dana, by all that was obvious, had made a lifelong habit of doing it the other way. Even in retirement he ordered his day with a cool self-discipline, assigning a proper segment to managing his portfolio, reading his books, entertaining his guests. Whatever fires of passion there once were no longer disturbed his routines, if they ever did.

But more depressing to me than my own disorders was the growing recognition that Dana and I were from different molds. I became aware as the days passed that he would remain for me a remote figure.

XII

AS my first spring at the Danas' came on, Washington was girding itself for renewed battle. This time the forces for military preparedness sought to impose a further advance of weaponry upon the forces who would rather do "better" things with the money. The press wrote excitedly about the "Great Debate." Some scribes were hinting ominously at "governmental deadlock" and "constitutional crisis." But columnist Mann assured me that these were standard clichés for every big political joust.

The approach of battle undeniably brought a lusty smell to the corridors of Congress. The men of politics seemed to perk up, purge their constipations, take on a new spring in the gait, a new flush in tired old cheeks, a new sparkle in their prose. A new vocabulary came into being and even the society matrons dutifully made efforts to master phrases like "counterforce," "second-strike capability," and "kill rate." One could overhear Senators in the Dana salon echoing the theories developed by the new breed of strategic planners.

102

To escape my drudgeries in the Dana household, I attended the Senate hearings where the issue was to be thoroughly aired. There was an opening solemnity to these proceedings in the great Caucus Room where the Senators sat elevated like judges and peered down on the testifiers below. The subcommittee chairman was Thomas Truesdale, the recanted militarist. My notebook reports:

> *Truesdale gravely assures us "This is a solemn occasion as we meet to decide an issue that could prove fateful to the life of the Republic. We mean to leave no stone unturned." But stones are not only turned. They are hurled back and forth as the hearings depart from any show of judiciousness. Senators mingle freely with the advocates. There is no dividing line.*
>
> *"This is the way it is and always has been," Mann tells B. "It is an adversary proceeding being performed before the high court of public opinion."*
>
> *But who sets the rules and procedures? Who makes certain that all the evidence is aired? "That depends almost totally on the whim of the Chairman," says Mann. "If he is an impartial man he can impose a certain amount of order. But if he is a true believer himself—like old Truesdale here— there are no rules, no procedures. Only his fellow committee members can hold him in check. But they are obligated to him for too many favors. In theory, the press could censure him. In practice, the more controversy, the better we like it."*
>
> *A hapless Pentagon witness is subjected to a*

103

withering crossfire of interrogation. Apparently, his superiors have advised him when in doubt to play dumb. He performs his role to perfection. Finally, he is lassoed, thrown, and hogtied by one persistent line of questioning. Will he or will he not produce for the committee evidence showing conclusively that the Pentagon is conspiring with the White House on the matter under review? The witness sweats profusely and mutters something about relations with the White House being cloaked in "executive privilege." At the sound of this phrase, Chairman Truesdale snorts like an angry bull. "I hereby direct you to produce the documents specified by this committee or run the risk of being held in contempt of Congress," the Chairman intones. The witness, relieved to escape from this durance vile, promises to consult his bosses. So the day's proceedings come to an abrupt and frustrating conclusion.

Will this lead to a fundamental showdown between the two great branches of government? "Don't count on it," Mann answers with a derisive laugh. "These tests come about once a week. To hear them talk you would think the President and Congress are locked in a life-and-death struggle over prerogatives. Then they meet in the back rooms and work out a compromise. Old Truesdale has made his point. He simply wanted to drag the White House into tonight's news leads."

I was excited over being a front row spectator in this Washington war. The opening stages, veterans of earlier ones pointed out, were exercises in thrust and maneuver. Each side sought to expose the other's weaknesses, all the while feeling out how strong were the bonds holding together its own forces. Various lieutenants took forward positions. A military man from the Pentagon tested an argument so horrendous that it outraged the public sensibility. He was pulled back in temporary disgrace. A lobbyist for the peace force became too explicit in spelling out the need for "trust" among nations; his troops groaned over the damage he had done them. Each side accused the other of ambiguity—of failing to admit its ultimate ambitions. And both were right, for neither side was willing to face ultimates. The military-might boys would not confess how much was enough, and the peace lovers would not say how little was too little. A conscious civility marked these opening stages. But before long passions grew hot and politicians were openly accusing one another of sins bordering on treason.

Looking on, I attempted to compare what was like and unlike the political struggle watched by Henry Adams when he first came to Washington. Adams was witnessing the efforts of the politicians to grapple with the terrible forces moving the nation toward civil war. Adams never really worked out a theory of history to explain that war: whether it could have been averted by strong and wise and moral leadership or whether it was the predestined outcome of history's unbending course. As a renegade Southerner, I have always believed that slavery was a curse that had to be expunged. But I have also believed there must have been a better way to accomplish this than war. Where I grew up, that awful war still stirs the passions and prejudices of those who go on denying its outcome.

Were Calhoun and Sumner and Seward the puppets of history or did these men fail history? And what about the current politicians who were now busily staking positions on this issue of life-and-death importance to the republic? I noted that a new dimension was added to political warfare by the advent of the monster weapons. Politicians now were speaking in apocalyptic rhetoric once reserved for evangelists. "Do it my way or you will be responsible for the death of mankind," argued the advocate on either side of the argument. It was producing a predictable effect. Constant exhortation was dulling the sense of terror and thereby losing political—even as it long ago lost evangelical—utility.

There were familiar features to this battle. The polls showed public opinion was evenly divided on the issue with the customary high percentage marked "undecided." I felt sorry for the politicians and began to wonder whether the pollster is ever able to tell them what they really need to know: How firmly has John Q. Citizen made up his mind and what will it take to change him? Of two John Q.'s, pro and con, which one cares more deeply? The pollsters, lacking a thermometer capable of really measuring public fever, must leave the politician to other devices—counting his mail, consulting his constituents, relying on that mystical perception which makes him a politician in the first place.

As I watched, I became aware of a strange thing. Mostly, the politician was relying on the echo chamber of the press to tell him which way the battle was going. This struck me as odd at first, for the politician would seem to be listening only to himself and his colleagues when he scans the newspaper column inches. But then I learned that he knows news can be tampered with. Skilled forces work at tilting the news one way or the other. How well they succeed helps decide the judgment rendered by the great god "public opinion."

Only to eavesdrop on a conversation among the politicians proved this proposition. Each one reads the newspaper and watches the evening roundups with a practiced eye. Who scored today? By how many column inches or video microminutes? How long will that particular news angle continue to claim the headlines? A musician, if he must create music on a piccolo, has to make his tunes shrill. So it is for those who make their careers creating public opinion. They must be expert in knowing the limits of the communication instruments they rely on.

My notebook records a chance encounter with one of the leading instruments of communication:

> *Edward Clifton, this evening's visitor at the Danas', comes from the curious breed known as television pundits. He appears nightly on the network news and his recitative of the day's events reaches many more millions regularly than the words of any ordinary statesman, even the President. It is an immense responsibility he bears and his dour expression seems to reflect that fact. One imagines all sorts of pressures, external and internal, to claim his attention and win his favor. He knows the politicians are watching for each intonation of a syllable, each arching of an eyebrow. He is not a handsome man, but he has a face that seems totally incapable of masking deviousness. An honest, open face such as belongs to barbers and choirmasters.*

107

Years of walking the uncertain line of impartiality has had its effect on Clifton. He has developed substitutes for fervor. He bites off his words and spits them at his viewers, creating the widespread impression that he cares deeply. But nobody can be sure about what. There are moments when he looks as if he is about to laugh or cry, or both, over the foolish state of the nation. He has enormous appeal to the millions.

Here in the privacy of the Dana salon, B finds that Clifton's mask does not really conceal much. Evidently, what goes on inside has long since rearranged itself to accommodate his TV image. Once he does voice a nostalgia for the good old days when he was a newspaper reporter and could cover live news with the rest of the boys. Now, he remarks ruefully, he attracts more attention than the politicians when he attends the Senate hearings. But B gets the feeling that being a celebrity is not keeping Clifton awake nights.

As I examined all the intricacies of this Washington war, I began to worry about the age-old dilemma of democracy. How much should the people decide? How much should be left to the leaders? Surely a point of absurdity had been reached when public opinion was expected to pass judgment on the complicated issue of strategic weapons even though the scientists, the strategists, and all the other experts could not agree among themselves.

Why not let the President decide? I had only to pose this question to realize how repugnant to American politics is the notion that a President should really be boss. There was also a more telling rebuttal. On issues like this one, what the President decided would not prove right or wrong until long after he had departed office. So why should he have the prerogative?

Several times I tried to air these dilemmas with Dana. The old man always offered incisive comments about the issues in dispute. But then one day it occurred to me that Dana had no more certitude than I about what was the right answer or even what was the right way to reach that answer. A lifetime in the high echelons of decision making had not given him these answers. All he had achieved was his cool detachment, which came perhaps from knowing that no one had *the* answers.

As usual, Mann summed it up the most trenchantly: "Our trouble, dear boy, is that we cannot afford the luxury of appearing in doubt. The great American people want father figures in Washington. They want absolute certitude from their leaders as well as their columnists. They will condone no hand-wringing. And when they change their minds on an issue, they want to follow a new leader who shows the same certitude."

The great debate continued. One evening when the Dana salon convened, Senator Truesdale had publicly accused the Pentagon of "deliberately concealing" data on the new weapon which would be detrimental to its case. Secretary Topping had counter-punched by releasing heretofore secret statistics on how many cities would be gutted by the enemy's opening attack. Out of the mishmash of facts and figures, out of shifting arguments of experts and amateurs, out of the confusion of hearings and press conferences, the great republic was moving toward a consensus. And in my notebook I recorded the following episode:

> *Dame Dana mixes her guests well. Tonight, the dinner table resounds loudly with the day's arguments on "weapons balance." Then, over the liqueurs, one Congressman's wife, a young woman noted more for beauty than brains, raises another problem. Her young son's male puppy suffers a hormone deficiency which is making him the catamite for every other male dog in the neighborhood. Her veterinarian warns that hormone shots could cause him to become the sexual aggressor. What to do? Solemnly, the politicians turn their deliberations to the pros and cons of hormone treatment. When the party breaks up at eleven, the issue of the perverted pet has taken precedence over the preposterous weapons.*

XIII

ON a fine morning that first spring Dana decided at the last minute to accept an invitation to a White House ceremony, taking me along. The limousine carried us through the Northwest gate right up to the West Wing, where guards and black-suited ushers greeted the old man with the effusive cordiality shown by functionaries at a gentleman's club. Inside the lobby, a threesome of secretaries on their way to lunch welcomed him as though he were the prodigal son. "We miss you, Mr. Dana. We surely do miss you," they chanted as they hurried off. A cluster of reporters looked up curiously from where they were lolling on the sofas, waiting to be spoon-fed the morning's news.

It was my first time inside the White House and I remember it clearly. In order to show me the place, Dana took me a roundabout way along the narrow corridor past the doorway to the President's Oval Office. As he paused to exchange handshakes with an aide, I felt the sudden knotting of stomach muscles that comes with being so close to the center of things. We were permitted to pass through the

111

Cabinet Room, more intimate than I had imagined, out French doors, and along the portico to the Mansion. The Rose Garden was ablaze with blossoms and beyond the sweeping south grounds gave a pastoral atmosphere to this house in the heart of the city. I remember thinking that a President ought to be able to forget his troubles strolling around such a park even if tourists were gaping at him through the iron fence.

We ascended the marble stairway and passed through the Mansion's entrance hall where red-and-blue-uniformed Marines played stirring tunes. Bright-colored rooms opened off in all directions. I had not dreamed this house could be so splendid. Not the rococo nineteenth-century splendor of the Capitol, but a simple splendor more familiar to the eighteenth century. We were ushered into the East Room, a golden place of large and graceful proportions. Soon after we took our seats, an usher came up and handed Dana a note, pointing across the room to where Senator Connar waved a greeting. Dana let me read it. "What the hell is a renegade like you doing here? Your fellow renegade, Connar." Dana grunted good-humoredly and stuffed the note inside his pocket.

After a period of hushed suspense, a military aide, looking wonderfully self-important, announced the President of the United States of America and he entered to the somewhat pompous strains of "Hail to the Chief." For my first in-the-flesh view of the President, I had not known what to expect. I found myself fascinated by the man's face, larger than life, tanned, exuding vitality. He had the glow of the leader. No sign of the torment daily reported by the press. Here in his own house he seemed buoyed up by the noisy applause of his invited guests. Every inch President. It seemed to me that he could listen to such welcome and not imagine he had an enemy in the world. I watched Senator Connar smiling and applauding with the rest. Everyone was smiling. There appeared to be a contest of smiles among those gathered in this room. "The capacity to smile," Henry Mann once assured me, "is the first requirement of the politician. To smile even when he is being kicked in his gonads."

The ceremony had been set to honor Elmer Skipton, a retiring semi-civil servant who had survived several occupants of the White House. Skipton had become, in fact, the symbol of the continuity of government despite the rise and fall of Presidents. Dana spoke favorably of him as a man with the true spirit for public service. He knew more than anyone else all the tiresome little details for getting things accomplished. It is surprising, Dana told me, how much these details can matter. "The President can get himself into all sorts of trouble merely issuing a new postage stamp if somebody doesn't pay attention to details."

This ancient retiree, I suspected, knew where a good many bodies were buried in the high places of government. Yet he had always preserved a discreet silence and now he was expected to go to his grave anonymously. A newspaper story that morning reported he had turned down a publisher's offer in "six figures" for memoirs carrying the title *My Thirty Years in the White House Basement*. The publisher had been quite prepared to hire someone else to do the actual writing. But Skipton said nothing doing.

So he was taking his leave with effusive praise. A bald, slightly stooped man, he stood throughout the ceremony

113

with a sour expression on his face which was likely meant to conceal his real emotions. Few men, I have observed, can hear themselves eulogized without choking up.

I was quite unprepared for the wit and humor shown by the President, having observed him through the stiffening medium of television. From his remarks delivered with such gusto, it was impossible to tell what was his, what should be credited to his speech writers. Dana pointed out several of them standing in the back of the room, laughing loudest at the jokes. Listening to this tribute, I was almost persuaded that genuine camaraderie exists among those who devote their lives to government. "Elmer Skipton knows the supreme satisfaction which comes to all men who serve the people," the President concluded fervently. Around the crowded room, one could feel the tightening of throats among politicians and civil servants alike.

Even the retiree looked like he was going to break down and cry. Humble to the end, he replied with a few faltering words of thanks and seemed vastly relieved when his wife was asked to stand and receive her share of the applause. Both giggled nervously when the President added a few last words of extemporaneous witticism: "After all, she deserves the real thanks. She's the one who loaned her husband to this demanding mistress that we all love so much."

It was a touching ceremony despite the corniness. Only once did the President depart from his good humor when, alluding to the growing opposition to his policies, he spoke sharply of "those who mollycoddle disaster." But that was enough. For days afterward, the news roundups were crackling with reports of his "bitter attack" on his opponents. All the generous words about public service got ignored

and what reached the public was the harsh sneering image
of an embattled leader. I wondered who had heard him
right—the amateur listener like myself or those reporters
trained to detect and amplify his slightest deviation from
the text.

Afterward, we joined the line along with Cabinet officers, Senators, and Congressmen, and filed past the President for a handshake. How could any man manage to clasp
that many hands and meet that many eyes? The President
had developed calluses in this activity and even affected a
hearty greeting as Connar came down the line. No on-
looker would imagine, watching these two, that one had
ever entertained an ill thought about the other.

At Dana's turn, the President greeted him with special
heartiness and then, while the rest of the line waited, took
him aside and spent a minute or so in earnest discussion. It
was sufficient to pique the press's curiosity. Over coffee
cups in the State Dining Room one reporter after another
sidled up to Dana seeking a confidential account of the
conversation. But he was not ready to abandon his secretive
habits. "The President expressed an interest in the state of
my health," he responded jokingly. "He wonders if exces-
sive leisure is having any harmful effects. I tried to reassure
him." A persistent female reporter was unwilling to let it go
at that. "Does this mean the President is getting ready to
call you back to active duty?" she asked. Dana was ready
for her. "The President knows a dead soldier when he sees
one." Maybe not much of an answer but it seemed to sat-
isfy the reporter.

I have often remembered this scene, the last time Dana's
path crossed the President's. Those two men with their

heads bent close, the President talking and Dana quietly listening. While there was little that was unusual about it, still I was impressed by how very personal is the business of leadership at the very top. The two could in truth have been discussing the state of Dana's health. Or they could have been exchanging views on a major policy issue. For a President lives his job whether seated at the council table or standing in a receiving line.

No matter how many times I review this scene, I cannot peer beyond the masks. There appeared to be affection there, or at least confidentiality. The two men seemed comfortable with each other. One, relaxed, quiet, a man accustomed to retirement; the other tightly strung with sense of duty. I noticed their hands. Dana's remained calmly at his side while they talked. The President's were never idle, jabbing, pounding, pointing and, finally, palms up in apparent entreaty. Those hands were trying to tell a story of their own, but of what I could not be sure. Then, there were the eyes. Dana's gray-blue eyes never wavered from the President's face but still they kept a distant remove. The President's were always searching Dana's face, seeming to look for any telltale clue not revealed by words.

Or so it seemed to me. I was beginning during this period to imagine more than I could really know. I was obsessed with the image of Dana. Frequently I would be roused in the very early morning, as if summoned by an alarm clock, to find that my sleep had been spent turning over and over some random idea about his life. Lying there, halfway toward waking, I found it difficult to distinguish between what I had heard or seen or read and what I had dreamed. More and more I became a victim of fantasy.

116

One episode made my imagination go wild. An associate of Henry Mann, arguing that I should get to know the "working press," arranged a get-together with several reporters who had covered the White House during Dana's day. So we gathered in the comfortable lounge of the National Press Club and sat underneath the huge portrait of a reclining nude and drank away most of an evening. While the news tickers played their incessant rhythm in a nearby alcove, I learned an amazing thing. These men whose business was facts, once liberated from the confining discipline of their typewriters, were capable of fantasies far beyond my own capacity. They solemnly swapped tale after tale about Washington which, if translated into newsprint, would have confounded the nation. Each sought to top the story of the other. I was reminded of bull sessions during college days when, to hear us talk, there was not a virgin within two hundred miles of Harvard.

A wizened fellow named Rutherford stood out from the rest. I read his copy regularly in a local paper, usually finding it rather stilted and dull. There, sprawled on the leather settee in the Press Club, puffing furiously on his big Havana, Rutherford was transformed into a spellbinder. His anecdotes sparkled. "Remember, Bohun," he declared with a sweep of his hand soliciting the assent of his colleagues, "the official story they tell you is never the real story. In my thirty years around this town, I've learned that lesson more times than I care to count." The others nodded affirmation.

I broached my obsessive subject. They believed—or professed to believe—that Dana's break with the President had been a nasty affair. The President, finding himself in a mounting predicament at home and abroad, had called on

117

Dana to play a role which was offensive to him. Dana had told the President to go to hell. There had been an ugly scene. The President tried both threat and bribery, reminding Dana of all the past honors accorded him. But Dana stood firm.

"You can be damn sure it was pretty dirty business," Rutherford assured me. "Otherwise, why would they go to so much trouble covering it up? I always thought old Dana was a hypocrite to pretend afterward that everything was sweetness and light. He went into exile without a whimper."

One reporter, whose name I have blessedly forgotten, was prepared to top Rutherford. He had the explanation for why Dana kept his silence. "That son of his was a queer. He came to a messy end and old Dana was always afraid they might drag the facts out in public." How did he know this? "I have my sources," he answered smugly.

How much of what they said was truth? It was hard to question the credibility of these men who spend their days watching the nation's politics at first hand. They make their living at it. But I was vaguely troubled by their vision of Washington. Perhaps having too many drinks at the Press Club unleashed the frustrated novelist that was lurking within each one of them.

But this was the fantasy with which these members of the White House press corps lived. Long afterward, when I was better able to isolate fact from exaggeration, I had cause to marvel at their inventiveness. Or was what I learned later really the truer version? It was the version put together from the direct observations of men intimately connected with the White House. But maybe they, too, had their fantasies. Maybe no one who works in the thin upper atmosphere of the Presidency is capable of perceiving the truth and nothing but the truth. Maybe not even Presidents.

Often between sleeping and waking, I shared the dark fantasy of these reporters. A fantasy where two men, stretched to the breaking point, uttered angry words and swore bitter oaths. Where Dana stormed forth from the President's office vowing never to return again. Where the nation's highest politics threatened to come apart in the clash of two strong personalities. Where only brutal blackmail kept the uneasy silence. My imagination conjured up every awful possibility.

Then with wakefulness, I remembered that final meeting between the two men, heads bent close together, engaged in earnest discussion. And I found that I could not reconcile my fantasy with this quiet memory.

XIV

March 30, A.D. 1

B turns thirty tomorrow. The event will be cele-brated modestly for he has not forewarned anyone nor does he intend to. No roll of drums nor swell of trumpets at reaching the second stage of manhood. The purposeful thirties. Now is the time man puts aside his childish toys and moves to the main game of life.

Jesus Christ began his preaching mission at thirty. Henry Adams was about to take a teaching post at Harvard. Chester Dana had already made his first million. But what of David Bohun?

In the morning's mail come birthday cards from his mother and his insurance man. The latter prides himself on never missing a milestone in a custom-er's journey through life. His mother's card, store-bought with a flowery tribute, revives sticky re-membrances of home. "Dad and I miss our son. We

120

are so proud of him but so lonely for him." B feels swelling within him the mingled sentiment toward home—nostalgia for the childhood love that once lived there, fear and faint embarrassment at efforts to revive it. He freely admits to himself that as a son he is worse than a failure; he is a disaster. Most young men are so good at faking filial obligation, playing up to Mama so that all who behold can say, "There is a good and loving son." But B cannot fake what he does not feel. He would like to believe this is because his true feelings are too genuine to permit deceit. But he is not sure. Does B love his father and mother? He is certainly full of guilt feelings toward them, acutely aware that he should love all the love they have heaped on him. But does he really love them? Or is he ashamed now that he has gone to Harvard and his father still says, in teasing, "He don't respect his old man any more." He doesn't *respect his old man, Father. For Christ's sake, why can't you make the mental effort to get your conjugations right?*

Even exploding inwardly produces the inevitable remorse. Maybe this tired old man can't master the King's English. But he supplied the seed that brought you into this world, David Bohun. And he never complained about the burden of pushing the first Bohun through college, which was a costly enterprise despite the scholarships. Maybe it wasn't love that made him bear the burden—but pride comes pretty close to love. He was proud of his son and now, confess it, his son is ashamed of him.

121

Back in the recesses of early memory, there was the Sunday morning's getting ready for church when the three of them shared the bathroom together and he had to do number one and looked over and saw his mother putting on her petticoat. B still remembers a sickly embarrassment at this intimacy. He never wanted to look at his mother's body even though, voyeur at an early age, he yearned to catch the fleetest glimpse of any other female's. Why was this, Dr. Freud? Couldn't he do his mother the honor to lust after her like a normal son? What was wrong with B's Oedipus complex?

The preacher's son across the street gave him the garbled facts about sex but it was the preacher's daughter, already nine when he was eight, who displayed the wares. At her instigation, they used to disappear behind the garage where amid the hot summer smell of nasturtium they meticulously inspected each other's ornaments and orifices. Then, one afternoon, his mother interrupted their idyl and, rather than seeking vengeance, took them for a visit to the local zoo. It was good therapy and he never again undressed the preacher's daughter. But the curiosity about female anatomy continued and grew stronger. In junior high, he got a look at his first pornography, a cartoon book of Winnie Winkle carrying on as she never did in the daily newspaper. The crude line drawings aroused him as hotly as if he had been there in the flesh with Winnie spreading her legs and inviting him to come touch.

He never got a chance to touch until he was a

122

college freshman on a football weekend when he was one of the drunken revelers gathered for midnight coffee at Hayes Bick. He learned later that she had a budding reputation as a nympho but that night, aglow with fish-house punch, he thought his charms had turned the trick. They broke parietal rules sneaking up a back stair to his room. It was over before it well began but that didn't keep her from putting him through the cold sweats when her period didn't come on schedule. He was never entirely sure which had bothered him more: this sordid introduction into the mystery of sex or the nagging fear of how he would have faced a blessed event. When Dana was dallying with the secretarial-school student, did they ever go through the agony of the missed monthly? Did he ever contemplate a lifetime beside a woman with whom sex would be the only nexus?

But what of Bohun? Whose fault is it that he has reached thirty without attaining a normal relationship of love and marriage? He has tried to untangle the skein of emotional involvements with his mother. In her, he sees all his own naïveté, his striving after poetic feeling, his wild yielding to impulse. It is what he hates in himself. And yet he sees too a stubborn, resourceful woman who against every odd has made her own life endurable.

Now he is thirty and who should be ashamed of whom?

123

XV

I HAVE no record of my first meeting with Pascal Dana—
of what I felt for her, of what she taught me about her
father, and to use the trite expression, about life. Sometime that first autumn she came home for a weekend's leave
from what she called the "female penitentiary" where she
served her time in the rolling hunt country of Virginia. My
impressions, I recall rather vividly, were not ecstatic: a slim
girl, dark blonde hair, brushed back, a face which just
missed beauty. Or rather it took time to trace the beauty of
that face, the mysterious, almost haunting enchantment of
those cool gray distant eyes—her father's eyes *sans* the bristling brows—and the fascinating symmetry of eyes, nose,
and mouth. Her mouth was the real triumph, inherited
from some earlier ancestor, full and warm and tempting . . .
but I am jumping ahead of my story. My first impressions
were decidedly unfavorable and this, like everything else af-
fecting Pascal's life, was because she willed it so.

I had gone to the upstairs library to pick up books Dame
Dana wished delivered to a friend. (Already my services

were extending to include messenger, dog walker, and houseboy.) The Dame was working at her desk and nearby the daughter sat buried in a book. At her mother's casual introduction, she raised her cool eyes for only the barest moment. Not even the trace of a smile flickered on those lips I later found so lovely. Then she resumed her reading and I, dismissed, went about my chores.

The winter passed with brief encounters that no longer linger in the memory. But I shall never forget the first real meeting. Spring came prematurely to Washington that year. It was early April but already the forsythia was festooning the Dana gardens and that night the dining-room windows had been thrown open wide to welcome the liquid sweet air. Pascal was home for the weekend and, for the first time, I found myself seated next to her when the inevitable party gathered round the dining table. Had she planned it that way?

This was already a low period in my steady descent into self-doubt. It seemed that every time I opened the literary supplements there were yardsticks thrust in my face. Others were producing. These comparisons served to produce a state of panic. Time was passing and I had scarcely begun.

"Tell me, Mr. Bohun, how does one go about preparing for a career as kept biographer?" It was the first nonperfunctory remark Pascal Dana had ever addressed to me, spoken in low confidential tones, the intended slur almost hidden it was delivered so innocently. But my thin skin had grown sensitized so that far less of a prick could cause hideous hurt. Pain followed by a hot flash of anger made me reckless.

"The first thing you have to learn is to endure the snotty

125

offspring you run across," I muttered. "Great men have a penchant for producing them."

She took it well. *"Touché.* So you have reached the conclusion that my father is really a great man. I would be interested sometime to have you tell me why."

This last was dealt out with the same lyrical lilt that left one wondering how much was in earnest, how much simply banter. I glanced sideways to find her appraising me with those calm gray eyes and again felt the flush of anger. "My contract doesn't require me to make any explanations. In fact, it doesn't even require me to conclude that your father is a great man if you have evidence to the contrary."

Aphrodisiac was in the air that evening combining with the whiskey and the wines to make me helplessly drunk. After dinner, I sought out Pascal and belligerently asked if she would walk in the garden. To my surprise, she consented almost demurely. For a long time we wandered through the dark maze of boxwoods, breathing in the freshening spring smells, each pursuing separate thoughts. I must confess that in my state of frustration the thought kept recurring that this was not an unattractive young woman by my side.

What could she have been thinking? We reached the summerhouse in the depths of the garden and stealthily, as if by prearranged consent, went in. The moon was full that night for I could make out her features plainly. A slight smile seemed to be playing on her lips and again I felt those eyes fixed on me. I had laid firm plans about how to renew the dinner-table conversation but the combination of air and alcohol and longing was too much. In amazement, I watched as Bohun's arms reached out and lightly cradling

126

Pascal Dana pulled those full lips toward him. He encountered no resistance.

In the telling, it seems unbelievable that so much happened in so swift a time. Whose lips first parted, changing this tentative brush into deep probing? Whose body made the first thrush of contact, pelvis hunched to grind against pelvis in the urgent rhythm? Bohun's wildest dreams had never counted on such a conquest and yet here he was, captor or captive, in a play of passion that raced toward the climax. After the long celibacy, Bohun's pent-up sex revealed itself with a prowess he never knew he had. But I, the silent observer, could not help noting that Pascal Dana, demure, aloof daughter, matched Bohun every step of the way. It was she, breaking off the embrace, who dragged out the chaise mattress from the storage closet; who stretched out on the floor of the summerhouse; who with sure, swift hands guided him, awkward, trembling. And thrust for thrust for flesh satisfying thrust, she stayed with him till the final rending burst.

Whose doing was this? Even now, so many times afterward, I hesitate to pass final judgment. Perhaps she, too, was responding to frustrations that went far beyond the bounds of plan or cunning. I would like to think that this is so, for I became devoted to the strange, tormented girl and, like all lovers, tried to remake her in the image I would have wished for her.

But I must be honest in this—my accounting—which is my first devotion. Even during the height of Bohun's passion, my mind's eye watched and knew that his blood lust was not alone. I am not unpracticed in the gentle art of seduction, and have by steady, slow persistence broken down

127

a companion's reluctance. But the silent sport whose opening round we staged that night was not seduction. Neither was it, by any stretch of the imagination, rape. Many, many times, as we lay exhausted and spent during the brief afterglow, I concluded that it was simple single-minded fornication.

One Pascal trait, even more curious than the total giving to the act of sex, was the total withdrawing once it had been consummated. I observed it that first night as I watched her there on the chaise pad. Suddenly she had risen, straightened her dress, brushed back her hair, and, without a word, was ready to depart. No hint of guilt or recrimination. Simply that the act was over and now it was time to get on with one's business without even the courtesy of a parting embrace. When we rejoined the party in the main house, Pascal neither by word nor look betrayed that anything had passed between us. I must confess to having felt a sense of relief that old man Dana would not suspect that I had taken his daughter. At the same time, there was a feeling of regret, of inadequacy, that my best efforts had produced no more lasting effect.

Still, as I said, this was only the first time. Each weekend visit, our affair took up where it had left off. Pascal set the timing and the place. To my delight, she too was partial to the morning hours, often entering my gatekeeper's cottage while I worked at my papers, and with scarcely a word of hello signifying she was ready. By daylight, I discovered womanly grace in Pascal's body, more than her severe schoolgirl clothes had allowed my imagination. I loved to lie upon my bed as she disrobed—she never liked assistance—and contemplate the adventure ahead for

128

Bohun. Make no mistake, she was an avid adventuress in the territory of sex. No two encounters were alike. Bohun found himself engaging in gymnastics that he had not thought himself capable of. There were times when he suspected she resented having to be entered rather than entering. She more than made up for her disadvantage by stage-directing each new version of how it was done to her.

After initial shyness in exposing his crippled leg, Bohun soon joined fully into the spirit of Pascal's play. Variety was the spice for her. On occasion, they would lather themselves in sun oils, attempting the maximum lubricated rub as if to turn their entire bodies into sex organs. Sometimes they would race to set new speed records, portal to portal, her fleet fingers helping to tease him on. And then they would test how long the act could be drawn out though Pascal, never very good at taking things slowly, would soon quicken the tempo that led to his undoing.

She showed strange transformations from beginning to end. Once aroused, this woman's reserve fell away completely; she became puppylike in enthusiasm, in curiosity, in appetite. But when it was over, the veil dropped down and she returned to the mystery inside herself.

Pascal was not alone in keeping this strange remove. Even as I recite this, I yield once again to my obsession for putting Bohun into the third person. There were in reality four of us, two spectators and two actors, whenever we gathered in that tiny gatekeeper's bedroom, in the summerhouse at the foot of the garden, or, more and more as the hot summer nights came on, bare under the open sky. We took brazen risks with exposure during those outdoor sorties but Pascal, once the obsession seized her, never seemed to mind, never even stopped to look round and wonder whether other voyeurs might be present. Bohun, finding release for all the desperate uncreativity trapping him, was hardly the one to urge caution.

So it was one evening we dined on the Shoreham Terrace and afterward, as passion once again fired to quick white heat, wandered down into Rock Creek Park and found seclusion on the grassy bank near the great concrete piers of the Calvert Street Bridge. Afterward, Pascal looked up at the majestic span echoing a steady roar of traffic, and remarked abruptly, "My brother jumped off that bridge. They found his body just about where we are."

Even now, I find it difficult to sort my mingled feelings —of excitement that my biographical venture was yielding unexpected fruit, of curiosity that Dana's orderly career had contained this dark disordered secret, of horror that she had so casually desecrated the tragic spot. Perhaps the horror of it had unsettled Pascal, too, for this was the first time she remained unveiled. She had loved her brother, three years her elder, with as much intensity as she did not love her father and mother. His death left a wound not yet fully scarred over. She found words of poetic aptness to describe the slim, sensitive youth who came of age in a household where success, so she said, was such an overbearing taskmaster.

"Peter was not meant for father's kind of success. He had his own talent—as a mimic, if you like. One twitch of his shoulders, one expression of his face, one inflection of his voice could describe someone better than a thousand words."

In her tumbled release of emotions long pent up, I learned the details of a tragedy that was years in the making. Peter had been a precocious boy, high-spirited, showing unusual promise in the verbal skills. There had been long separations from his busy family during childhood and adolescence, winters at boarding school, summers at camp. Evidently he lacked for nothing except the love he yearned for most. He had been expelled from prep school for displaying unusual skill in drawing and circulating pornography among his classmates. Nursed into college with the help of a rigid military academy, he promptly proceeded to get turned off by the whole process of education. He did nothing bad. He simply did nothing at all. When the accumulation of failures finally caught up with him, he returned home on extended leave. For more than a year, he worked as attendant in a local automobile service station, departing faithfully each morning in his coveralls and returning each evening as a silent, subdued spectator in the Dana mansion. No, there had been no violent scenes of parental outrage that Pascal could remember. Her mother had a persistent way of reminding Peter that time was passing, that he really ought to be getting back to his books. But Chester Dana kept his silence, apparently resolved to let the son find himself in his own good time. "Anger would have been better. At least he would have known that somebody cared enough to get mad," Pascal assured me. There had been no anger, only the self-contained detachment that was the prevailing spirit in the Dana family. With his younger sister, who was beginning to discover the strange torment of sexual flowering, Peter did share an intimacy. And that, too, I gathered

131

from things Pascal left unsaid, had created deep guilt for there must have been moments when their longings went beyond chaste notions of brother-sister relationship.

So Peter Dana's life had ended one spring evening under the Calvert Street Bridge. The police, noting that his pockets were empty of valuables, had speculated that he might have been shoved off by a street gang known to be terrorizing that neighborhood. Washington was caught up in foreign crisis at the time and quickly pushed the Dana boy's death to the back burner of parlor gossip.

Henry Adams, upon his wife's suicide, banished her from his conversation and writings, even leaving a twenty-year gap in his autobiography to get round the tragedy of her death. But his has been judged an act of caring rather than callousness, and Adams later commissioned Saint-Gaudens to create a fitting memorial for her gravesite.

Chester Dana's grief followed a similar outward course. Once having established a scholarship fund in Peter's memory, he never again mentioned his son. Dame Dana, too, maintained a stoic composure. If she suspected that Peter's death was more than a random blow of fate, she kept it from the rest of the family.

Pascal had not forgotten or forgiven. For her, there was none of the romantic aura surrounding Henry Adams' vow of silence. "Life was supposed to pick up just where it left off, no better no worse now that Peter was gone. It killed whatever warmth I may have ever felt for my cold, cold parents." I suspected then that she premeditated our joust in Rock Creek Park, staged the love act on the spot where it would tear open the old wound, arranged her confession to have the greatest shock value on her father's biographer. And while she succeeded beyond all expectation, I could not help but wonder what kind of child could hate her father so.

XVI

I HAVE always found the act of self-destruction too hypnotic to spend much time pondering. What pushes a man to that final act of will—to leap the bridge's railing? Courage, cowardice, or lunacy? And, especially, what could drive a man so young? That same evening, I studied the photographs Pascal showed me of the slim, sensitive youth. There was a sadness about the eyes, a wide-eyed searching look that, knowing what I knew, could be described as haunted. But suicidal? No. He did not look like a youth who would deliberately destroy himself. There was the unmistakable Dana in the strength of his brow and chin. There was, in the more serious photographs, the resolutely earnest look of Dame Dana.

Late that night, spurred by fantasy, I put my troubled words on paper:

PETER'S SOLILOQUY

What does it feel like when the body hits the earth? That's a fearful thought but I fear even more

134

those moments of free falling with the brain still un-bruised, still anticipating what lies ahead.

For I am thinking calmly. This leap will not be made in frenzy. I am quite calm, quite clear in my own mind about what I'm doing. Perhaps this is the first clear thing I have ever done. There is irony here for I feel so clear and calm that I almost regret bringing it to an end.

Is it a chemistry in the blood? That would be comforting to know for then all blame would be absolved. But I could never know this unless perhaps I were to have one massive transfusion, pumping out the last polluted drop in exchange for purer stuff. It would be a laugh to tell my father, "Dad, my twenty-year-old blood is tired. I want fresh blood." He might not see the humor.

I don't believe new blood would do the trick. All my parts are corrupted, and maybe it isn't blood at all that caused the trouble. At dinner not long ago I heard a famous psychiatrist telling my father that he measures schizophrenics by how far they plan ahead. A patient capable of planning six months is ready to leave the asylum. I thought how funny that is for I can never even plan tomorrow.

I honestly don't remember when my walls began to crumble. Watching others move with so much certainty in their lives, I could not find that certainty in mine. I tried to imitate the others. But it didn't happen.

I have planned this act for more than six months. That's my last laugh, being so sane about this final

135

act of insanity. I am frightened to go but to stay would be more frightening still . . .

There I broke off and never resumed this particular exercise in imagination. I dared not go further.

XVII

THAT summer the elder Danas were roughing it once more at Pride's Crossing. It was not a period of relaxation for me. By now, I was driven by mounting anxiety to pursue my biographical quest. I hoped that Harvard would hold some of the important answers.

"Some universities have greater beauty and a richer past, some have maturer scholars and more famous teachers, Yale herself has more unity, more energy, and greater fitness to our present conditions. Harvard, instead of all these advantages, has freedom. . . ." This was the summing up of the poet and philosopher George Santayana and I never had cause to quarrel with his judgment. No Bohun had ever visited this far-off Mecca before me; few Bohuns, if it must be told, had even completed high school. But something in the blood as much as the brain caused my pilgrimage there. The day the letter came announcing that I was recipient of a Harvard scholarship designated for benighted Southerners —that day is marked in my memory.

The reality of Harvard was little less than the dream.

137

During those undergraduate years before learning began to cloy, I cherished Santayana's "freedom" in this ancient institution. Centuries ago, Harvard had broken loose from the tight bonds of dogma. For me, as for Thomas Wolfe and countless other Southerners, it offered liberation from provincial heritage. I felt rootless, free. If Sherman's army had marched straight through my spiritual home, I could not be more stripped of heirlooms.

It was a matter of place as well as mind. At Harvard, you felt free enough to stay sober on Saturday night if it suited you; indeed, free enough to spend the evening with a book. Many Harvard men, not in the least peculiar, did just that. At the same time, across the river beckoned Scollay Square where a professional voyeur like me could pay a modest sum and watch female flesh palpitating about the stage to the gentle rhythms of "A Pretty Girl Is Like a Melody." The Old Howard, venerable church converted to burlesque house, has closed its doors since my undergraduate years, but it was alive and thriving when Chester Dana was a student. Surely he must have found there the same surcease from overstimulation of the mind.

I must speculate on this, for it would have been presumptuous to query the old man about such frivolities. It was not part of our unspoken contract. Furthermore, Dana went to another Harvard from the one I attended. Not just of a different era, but of a different community. For in reality there are two Harvards, the one casting out a wide net for young men of promise whether they be Cabots or Cohens, white or black. This Harvard offers its best and pays lavish subsidies to get the most able of the nation's youth. But there is a different Harvard, separate and aloof,

138

which holds to a three-century tradition of aristocracy. It pursues the same studies, shares the same classrooms and lodgings. There the fraternization stops. It is a smaller Harvard, certainly not a tenth the size if measured in numbers.

A subtle and very silent process separates the two Harvards. There is none of the vulgar "rushing" pursued by fraternities in most universities; nor is it so ostentatious as the "tapping" for Skull and Bones and the other clubs at Yale. Instead, a small quota of the sophomore class is quietly invited into Hasty Pudding or Dickey. An even more select number of these make it into the "waiting" clubs. The elite of the elite move into the "final" clubs, of which Porcellian or Pig is the oldest and the most exclusive. Harvard's historian, Samuel Eliot Morison, has written: " [Porcellian] almost from its origin had been the goal of social ambition, and [its] practices and postures were imitated by all the rest."

This was the Club into which Chester Dana was invited. Porcellian traces its beginnings back to 1791 when a group of "choice spirits" met at a local tavern to dine on roast pig and decided to make a regular custom of it. Such was its prestige that Theodore Roosevelt announced his daughter Alice's engagement with the public boast that both he and her fiancé, Nicholas Longworth, had been fellow Pigs. Teddy, of course, belonged to the Oyster Bay Roosevelts; Franklin Delano, of the Hyde Park clan, failed to make Porcellian. Nor did J. P. Morgan, although a number of other Morgans as well as Frothinghams, Saltonstalls, Lodges, Wainwrights, and Wymans are listed on the club's rolls. Unlike Skull and Bones at Yale, Porcellian is secure enough in its traditions not to make a fetish of secrecy.

When I queried Dana about his membership, he appeared rather diffident. He was one of a long line of Danas to be taken in, including the celebrated author, Richard Henry Dana. But the others all came from New England ancestry to which he could trace no blood connections. He observed jocularly that it had been a good place to get a decent meal at a time when Harvard offered no dining halls. He exhibited little pride in this distinction and, so far as I observed, never carried the tiny gold pig which was proof of membership.

Yet it had made a difference. Even in the more democratic days when I reached Harvard, the club men were a breed apart. By then, undergraduates were obliged to take their meals in one or another of the university's dining halls. Still the club men kept to themselves, huddled in solitary little groups at mealtime and afterward drifted off to their splendid monasteries where they could consort with their own. Of an evening, I used to walk by these buildings and wonder about the rich and distant lives that were led within.

During the latter part of my senior year, I managed to get to know a clubman named Wentworth who was member of Porcellian. He was a handsome fellow, obviously a blueblood, and, what was surprising, he made the overtures leading to our brief friendship. He took to dropping by my room after dinner. "I like you, David. You care about the important things," he announced quietly. There was a strange glint in his eyes and I couldn't be altogether sure he wasn't pulling some club prank. Then the friendship was rudely shattered. Wentworth, an Episcopalian, had been converted by a local Catholic priest who was concentrating on

140

Harvard students. He had become a proselyte of the Pope. He found barren soil in me. But his faith drove him with a merciless intensity to quit Harvard only a few weeks away from graduation and join full-time with the local priest. Years later, I learned that the priest, along with Wentworth and a small band of brothers, had been branded heretics by the Vatican. The last I heard they were pursuing a rootless religion of their own making.

Wentworth was surely an exception. The majority of the small minority at Harvard who were clubmen appeared smugly content with the destiny that set them apart. They were not unfriendly to the rest of us, merely indifferent. Theirs was a system so select and so unobtrusive, as historian Morison observed, that it "inflicts no 'inferiority complex' on outsiders." I do not suggest that Porcellian was the whole of Chester Dana's existence at Harvard. Or that clubbishness was necessarily a constricting experience. Some of Harvard's more distinguished free spirits—John Reed, Roger Baldwin, Corliss Lamont, Cass Canfield— emerged through the club tradition. My point is simply that I was not of that tradition and therefore have difficulty interpreting one who was.

Dana came to Harvard in the aftermath of a great world war. His was a time when the whole nation was swelled with inflated ambitions about making the world safe for democracy and building permanent peace. By the time he left, the disillusionment had set in. Warren Gamaliel Harding occupied the White House. Narrow-minded normalcy had become the spirit of the day.

I dug through records in the Widener archives in order to

141

understand my man's college years. They came midway during the long reign of President Abbott Lawrence Lowell, the Boston Brahmin who did so much to build modern Harvard. Lowell believed with great passion in learning and strove to abolish the "gentlemanly C" as the norm for academic achievement. At the same time, he held that "moral training in college is quite as important as the academic instruction . . ."

Dana studied under men whose reputation as Harvard's "greats" lingered into my own time there: Charles McIlwain, Frank Taussig, William Hocking, Bliss Perry. He told me that he had fond memories of dropping in on the evening sessions at Hollis 15 where Charles Copeland—"Copey"—read aloud to his students and, in the words of one of them, "stimulated generations of men to find color and strength and beauty in books."

"No reasonable man could breathe the air of Harvard at this time and not feel free," historian Morison wrote. It was the era of public fears about the Bolsheviki, but Lowell allowed no witch hunts in his university. When outraged alumni demanded the scalp of Law Professor Zechariah Chafee, Jr., because he criticized Justice Department practices, Lowell coolly turned the matter over to Harvard's Visiting Committee—which concluded that Chafee had not been guilty of "conscious error." Before even more insistent pressures to fire a young visiting instructor from England, Harold Laski, for siding with the policemen in the Boston Police strike, Lowell threatened that he would resign first. The important moral in this for all Harvard men was that Lowell actually detested Laski, a left-wing Socialist, and all he stood for.

142

That was the way you felt freedom at Harvard. A furor arose during Dana's sophomore year over a speaking invitation extended to a young man, Wilfred Humphries, to report on his visit to Soviet Russia. After a bitter exchange in the letters column of the Harvard *Crimson,* the editors mediated the dispute by upholding the principle of free speech but concluding "Mr. Humphries is not the sort of man who should be encouraged to speak in Harvard Halls . . ." Perusing the pages of old *Crimsons* and other intramural literature, I sensed the swift tide toward complacency, swifter by far than during my own years following the Second World War. The auto had come to Harvard. There were splendid pictures of Pierce Arrows, Hupmobiles, and Packards available to a wealthy student clientele. Advertisements described lavish apartments on the Gold Coast with ornate ceilings, handsome brass chandeliers, and marble mantles. Dana shared one such apartment with several of his fellow Porcellians until, in his senior year, he took a solitary room in the Yard. For those lucky enough to be on the club lists there were invitations to debutante parties in Boston and environs where, despite Prohibition, champagne and cruder forms of alcohol flowed freely.

It was a time of new sexual freedom. After cogitation, the Harvard deans tried to curtail it by revising the ancient parietal rule that "No young woman unattended by an older woman should be received in a student's room." *Should* was changed to *may,* evoking great ridicule among the students.

How did young Dana fare at Harvard? I have no doubt that he sniffed the exciting air, so free of the musty smells back home; strolled through Harvard Square throbbing with commerce of the intellect; whiled away long evenings over books in Widener; perhaps, of a spring afternoon, lay on his back alongside the Charles River and dreamed of what the future would be like. Was he aware that *normalcy* had become the watchword for a nation's self-indulgence? Two Harvard students out of three voted in a straw poll to join the League of Nations during the first postwar enthusiasm. But by the next year nearly five out of eight cast their vote for Harding. The *Crimson* argued that "Most Harvard men trust the League issue with Senator Harding and they refuse to endorse a man who endorses Wilsonism." Harding's victory, declared the college paper, would mean that "The speedy entrance of the United States into the 'Association of Free Nations of the World' is assured beyond the possibility of rejection."

Tucked away in the letters column of next day's *Crimson,* I came upon Dana's one public utterance that I could discover during his years at Harvard. The epistle read in its entirety: "Sirs: At Des Moines recently Harding said, 'I do not want to clarify these [League] obligations. I want to turn my back on them. It is not interpretation but rejection I am seeking.' Those words would seem to refute your editorial. Sincerely, C. Dana."

That was all. The nation marched toward normalcy and the youth of Harvard seemed quite content to march along. If there were any laments about the sacrifice of ideals for which so many of the generation just ahead gave their lives, the printed record in Widener contains scarcely a trace of it. Young Oliver LaFarge was writing poignant tales about the plight of the American Indians in the Harvard *Advocate.* Both *Advocate* and *Crimson* editorials occasionally decried

144

the excesses of the Red Witch hunt, while conceding there was a problem of "foreign-born" agitators in the United States. So a great university, along with the rest of the nation, slipped into the second-rate expectations of the twenties.

Dana enjoyed the luxury that the clubman's Harvard offered to a chosen few. But he did not neglect academic Harvard and the official transcript shows his presence on the honor roll throughout his four years. Evidently in his junior year he made the firm resolve to excel in studies. This led to his degree *summa cum laude*.

I retrieved his thesis from the New England Repository Library and searched its pages for clues to the early Dana. The thesis was entitled "Failure of Conciliation: 1855–1861." In taut, clear prose, Dana traced the nation's movement toward civil war. He laid out a large canvas, tracing with even-handed impartiality the failures of vision both North and South that led to the great schism. He described failure of institutions as much as of men, of the church, the political parties, the Congress, the Presidency. Obviously, Lincoln was a hero figure to Dana even as Buchanan was a subject of contempt. But I got the impression that Dana's admiration was more for the agony endured by the Great Emancipator than for his capacity to shape the course of history. Indeed, there was a passionless quality to this opus, as if he accepted history's ineluctable working and merely sought to understand it better. He refrained from might-have-been. He told his story with discipline and detail remarkable in so young a scholar.

Commencement Day activities at Dana's graduation provide poignant reminders of what might have been if Amer-

145

ica had faced its responsibilities in the year 1922. Before a large audience gathered in Sever Quadrangle, Mordecai Wyatt Johnson, a young black man from Tennessee who was getting his degree as Master of Sacred Theology, gave the Commencement oration. Read this many years later, his speech was a prophetic account of his race's struggle to have faith in the American system. Describing a curiously impersonal "they" rather than "we," Johnson sounded the growing disillusionment of his race since the war. "With one voice, therefore, from pulpit and from press, and from the humblest walks of life, they are sending up a cry of pain and petition such as is heard today among the citizens of no other civilized nation in the world," he told the Harvard audience. "They are asking for the protection of life, for the security of property, for the liberation of their peons, for the freedom to sell their labor on the open market, for a human being's chance in the courts, for a better system of public education, and for the boon of the ballot."

Among those getting honorary degrees that morning was another Southerner, Oscar Wilder Underwood, Senator from Alabama, cited as "A Statesman of no common mold who has seen the duty that our country owes both to itself and to the world." Underwood had helped lead the bitter failing fight in Congress to ratify the Versailles Treaty. Now, in the second year of Harding, Harvard chose this way of paying tribute. The Senator spoke in the afternoon, still hopeful about beginnings made at the Washington Disarmament Conference earlier that year. But he warned darkly that "special interests" were at work in Congress which could destroy these efforts for a lasting peace. Even as he spoke, a torrent of rain drove his listeners to the shelter of nearby

146

buildings, in defiance of God's law that the sun should shine on Harvard Commencements.

"Four years of Harvard College, if successful, resulted in an autobiographical blank, a mind on which only a water-mark had been stamped." This was the cryptic judgment which my hero, Henry Adams, declared of his college train-ing nearly three quarters of a century earlier. Was he giving praise or condemnation? I am inclined to believe that Adams was really quite content that his mind had not been cluttered with learning but provided instead with a water-mark of quality. Perhaps the essence of an education is the capacity to select discriminatingly what shall be written on the blank sheet of one's mind.

That is the way it worked for Chester Dana. Again and again in his later life, I have had cause to marvel at the clarity of his thought processes. At times it could be mis-leading. One might conclude on superficial impression that Dana was impervious to the complexities that confuse most men's lives. But this conclusion would be wrong. Rather he had a mind which cut its way through complexity and, in the end, reduced complexity to its essential elements.

Henry Adams had known a Virginian as a classmate at Harvard, Roony Lee, the son of Robert E. Lee. Young Lee started out as the most popular and prominent man in his class but then gradually faded. "The habit of command was not enough and the Virginian had little else," Adams wrote much later, with the harsh and sweeping conclusion: "Strictly, the Southerner had no mind; he had tempera-ment."

Much as I respect Adams, I must argue that the Southerner had changed by the time Dana went to Harvard. I am not

147

at all sure what role Harvard played in Dana's educative process. The College was offering a bonbon box of elective courses. It was possible for the helpless undergraduate to become totally disoriented as he tried to put together a meaningful program of studies. But Dana avoided this. He learned to order his priorities and maybe that is the best thing that can happen to a man.

Certainly it didn't happen to me. Now as I look back on my college career, I can see clearly that I fell victim to false gods at Harvard. I learned there to create complexity out of what should be simple. I cultivated my verbal precocity and employed a thousand words where ten would do. And all the while I became less confident of cutting through to the heart of the matter, of reducing life's choices to the basic alternatives. Yet I cannot find it in my heart to condemn Harvard for this failure. For me, as for Dana, the University was a great laboratory where each man had near-absolute freedom to test his talents. Santayana was everlastingly right when he described "freedom" as the unique condition Harvard had to offer. The fault lies within ourselves if for one man freedom produces clarity and for the other confusion.

Even as I write this, I recognize that I may be succumbing once more to wordmaking. For I am by no means certain that Dana would have summarized his life as the triumph of clarity. He never said anything to me directly to the contrary, but still more than a small doubt exists. Perhaps Chester Dana, if he had ever indulged in autobiography during his declining years as Henry Adams did, might also have concluded that his education was a failure.

But I shall not jump ahead of my accounting. The time

148

is 1922 and America is moving irreversibly toward moral and later financial bankruptcy. And Chester Dana has just completed the requirements for a Harvard degree with every academic and social accolade that university can bestow. At commencement, he wore the red tassel of a class marshal. Dame Dana, there to watch her brother receive his degree, tells of the quietly modest young man, obviously well regarded by his classmates, marching forward with the elite group of *summa* recipients. That night the Rockwells invited Dana and his mother for a celebration feast at Locke-Ober's and there, in the sparse New England setting which I came to know and love, they exchanged farewells. Brother Tod was full of nostalgia for the college years now past. He would remain in Boston in textiles until his untimely death. But Dana was departing for New York and the world of finance. He did not seem sad, simply reconciled to the fact that one chapter was closing and another about to begin.

I tracked down Arthur Boyden, Dana's tutor during his undergraduate years, now finishing a long career as professor *emeritus* in a small New Hampshire college. Boyden still had the twinkle of the good teacher about him. He remembered Dana well, spoke glowingly of the "quiet grace," the "effortless competence," and the "unseasonable maturity" of his youthful protégé. He had urged Dana toward a career in scholarship, never doubting that he would have risen to the first ranks. But Dana had not been tempted by this prospect. He already had his eyes fixed on Wall Street.

Why did he think Dana turned his back on the scholar's career? Old Professor Boyden sucked for a time on his heavily caked briar pipe. When he replied, the twinkle had

149

gone out of him. "Maybe there was a certain passion lacking. A certain conviction. Maybe he concluded that scholarship had nothing to offer at the time he was coming out of college—and maybe he was right."

XVIII

THAT fall I began my second year with the Danas. Nothing was changed, but the longer I stayed, the more I found myself baffled by questions of style and substance. Which was the more essential in the politics of this capital city? I was disturbed by Professor Alton Sharp, a regular visitor in the Dana salon. At close hand, he showed himself to be a reckless fellow, intemperate in speech, overimpassioned. When he got roused, he indulged in arguments bordering on the lunatic. Yet all these faults were missing from his published prose. His words marched with solemn elegance across the page, making much use of metaphor, witty allusion, and subtle irony. By grace alone, words had won him a wide audience and considerable influence in Washington. On the other hand, I met many men of superior insight who were consigned to oblivion because their prose was turgid.

Another visitor, John Netter, was praised by Dana as one of Washington's ablest administrators. Netter knew how to take a lazy bureaucracy and get things done. But put him on a lecture platform and he was hopeless. Once, called on to address a convention of women, he admonished the horrified ladies "We must strip away the fig leaf of Communist deceit and expose the bare bone of Communist intent." Failure of rhetoric, of style, had put a ceiling on his climb upward.

One evening, we were joined by Harold Wheeling, the prominent political cartoonist whose skill lay in bringing out the grotesque in public figures. My notebook records that Wheeling was childishly sentimental about his craft:

"Every man by the time he reaches maturity has made his own face," he declares. "My job is simply to discover the telltale character lines." But Wheeling has no good answer when Dana asks about the politician who happens to be born with narrow-set eyes or receding forehead. Dana presses home his point: "Not long ago I chanced to see the campaign poster of one of our more beautiful Senators. A rainstorm had warped the poster, causing the lower half to bow out ever so slightly. The effect was to give the Senator a chin like that of the Cro-Magnon man. Only a half-inch change made the difference. But the difference in real life could forever blight the Senator's ambition for higher office."

Has style always played so pervasive a role in the nation's politics? Mann argues that politician's hair styles grow long or short in inverse ratio to ladies' hemlines. But a more serious question is whether Abraham Lincoln's style would be acceptable to modern tastes. Would we idolize the poet-President

152

who seemed so uncouth to many of his own contemporaries?

Dana voices doubt that Lincoln would do well. The television tube is adding a new dimension to President-watching—a new premium on style as opposed to substance of leadership. Mann promptly declares himself television's bitter foe. "It has bastardized the art of leadership," he announces solemnly. "It has made Presidents into jugglers—ordinary circus jugglers."

This provokes a debate among the Dana guests whether television is opening the way for a new, more deadly form of political demagogy. "The potential is there," Dana concludes gloomily. "If the demagogue ever masters the formula for provoking public hysteria via the mass media, it will be more dangerous than fissioning the atom."

John Netter then gets to bellyaching about the press. It seems that a new policy he has carefully nurtured for months has been blasted into oblivion by a single newspaper story, leaked by a bureaucratic foe. The premature publicity brought orders from the White House: "Deny it."

Henry Mann, waxing self-righteous as spokesman for the free press, puts up a spirited defense. "My dear boy," he addresses the bureaucrat five years his elder, "you seem to think policy can be grown like mushrooms in a damp dark cellar. You are wrong. This is a democracy and the people have a right to know what you are doing for them or, should I say, to them."

153

But Netter gives as good as he gets. "And you think, Mr. Mann, that policy can be grown out on the corner of 14th and F streets. No reporter conducts his own affairs that way. No newspaper either. It's absolute rubbish to pretend that the people will suffer if they aren't told everything the minute somebody thinks of it. God, in His wisdom, decreed that a baby spends nine months in his mother's womb. But you journalists would pry right in there if you had your way."

Mann retorts that the bureaucrat utterly fails to understand the rules of the game. "You ought to do your own leaking before your enemies do. You forget that we are living in a jungle. It's survival of the fittest and I say more power to it."

This provokes an impassioned outcry from Netter that sound policy cannot survive such a game. "Too many facts have to be weighed. Too many experts have to be consulted. Too many bases have to be touched. But let a reporter get hold of a tiny piece of the story and the whole thing comes unglued. Sometimes I think the press regards the business of government as a sport intended for their personal amusement. It's damn irresponsible, that's what it is. It's . . . why it's goddamned subversive."

As the two sulkily break off, Dana appears wryly amused by the explosion. He comments that it is an age-old argument not having changed one whit since he first came to town. Neither government nor the press is prepared to understand the problems of the other. Reporters established their hunting rights

154

back in the earliest days of the republic. Even Thomas Jefferson could not make up his mind about how he felt toward an unfettered press.

"But what has changed," Dana points out, "is the balance between 'reality' and 'image.' A press corps, thousands strong, now works in Washington. It creates the daily picture of government for the public. Its picture becomes the reality on which the policymakers must act. Shadow shapes the substance it is supposed to reflect."

This provokes one last outburst from Netter. He complains bitterly that the reporters' vocabulary is woefully inadequate for their task. "They assign you an adjective early in your career. 'Smart,' 'Tricky,' 'Ruthless,' 'Wheeler-dealer.' It's a matter of chance which adjective you get. But once you've got it, all the powers of heaven and hell can't change it. They put it in their clip files and every time they do a story on you, out it comes. Washington is a city of one-adjective men, branded for life by the press."

I was having my own personal problems of shadow and substance that second winter. There were mornings when the act of picking up pencil became for me an exertion beyond my capacity. Not that I could not manage the heft of it. Once elevated, the pencil had to be laboriously pushed and pulled to trace the hieroglyphics of a word. And the word must stand for something, be part of a pattern revealing a mysterious process known as Thought. That was the rub, for at the very thought of Thought a malaise would

155

seize me. A numbness in the upper reaches of my skull. A feeling of fatigue in arm and leg. It was not physical—or at least not physical in origin—for I was doing absolutely nothing to warrant fatigue. Yet the symptoms could not have been more severe if I had spent my time on a road gang.

I used to try mental setting-up exercises in the desperate hope that gymnastics might clear the brain and loosen the muscles. Like a paraplegic, I would lift my pencil and haltingly write a word. That word often suggested its companion and soon I found myself hobbling down the literary road. I dared not look back. To keep my hard-won momentum was enough. Never mind the substance so long as I could manage the style.

What was Dana doing to me? By now my feeling of love that came from proximity to greatness had turned into a love-hate syndrome. I was no nearer the soul of the man than I had been the year before. I had begun to doubt he had a soul. Or if he did, had he sworn an awful pact with God to go to his grave without exposing it to my prying? I had never before encountered such an interior man. When I grew up, my father stormed and my mother wept and nobody held anything back. We used to tell each other our dreams. Of course, by the time I went away to college, I had acquired the habit of reticence. But it was more an awkwardness at being obliged to stand on display before my father's friends.

Dana's reticence was a different kind. He simply did not desire—no longer understood the desire—to share himself with others. I had concluded that this was not a game of hide and seek we were engaged in. I no longer suspected

156

that there was a single secret or a missing piece which, once located, would cause all his parts to fit together.

I realize now that this man was privately preparing his soul for its maker. But he was doggedly determined not to let anyone else share in those preparations. I resented being kept out of his private communion. There were so many questions that might have been answered if I had been permitted to eavesdrop. I am convinced that this was an important dialogue in Dana's life and that it had been going on for a long time. For he did hear inner voices and they helped him make the major choices of his career, including his tragic choice.

I had a dream one night that Dana really revealed himself. Rather it was more like a nightmare. It happened after we had spent a long evening as guests of Henry Mann at the annual White House Correspondents dinner. Gathered in the vast hotel ballroom, black-tied and well fortified with alcohol, was the self-selected establishment of the Washington press corps. With them sat hundreds of politicians, judges, upper-level bureaucrats, and elder statesmen. And, finally, there at the head table, arriving between the dessert and the entertainment and looking thoroughly miserable, was the President of the United States. Everybody knew he hadn't wanted to come. But this was power-of-the-press night. So he sat there glumly as the newly chosen leader of this august group delivered his inaugural speech. Traditionally, it was the chance to get back at the politicians for all the indignities inflicted on reporters, all the hours spent in outer offices waiting for crumbs of information, all the drivel that the politicians seek to purvey as news. The new leader either bore unusual grudges or had a macabre sense

157

of humor. He took advantage of the President's presence to enumerate the long list of sorrows afflicting the White House. Once in a while a drunken correspondent would whoop appreciation, but mostly the audience settled into astonished silence. The President, stony-faced, stared at his plate. Then, in a final heavy-handed thrust, the inauguree read an honor roll of the Chief Executive's "former" friends who were present that evening. When his name was called, Dana, who had sat silently throughout this graceless oratory, gave a derisive snort. The evening broke up early but I could not help noting—and admiring—that the departing President took pains to shake hands with his tormentor.

Later that night, I had my dream. Dana sat behind a small table as though being interviewed on a television panel show. But as the program moved along, he turned out to be in his own living room and I was the one doing the interviewing. What he said has been filtered out of my dream's recollection but at last he was giving a stream-of-conscious exposure of his inner thoughts. Eagerly I rushed forward to hear the revelations. Then, with horror, I discovered that it was not the Dana I knew. Rather it was a Chester Dana with the weak, wizened features of his brother Paul. He had even acquired his brother's whine. I listened to his long self-serving explanations which made me cringe with disgust. Dana was torn with indecision about his break with the President. He protested a malevolent fate. He was full of self-pity. Then, as I moved still closer to witness this sad spectacle, it was not Chester Dana at all. It was brother Paul who was talking and we

158

were back in the Richmond nursing home. And I felt suddenly relieved by the fakery of dreams.

We are so irrational in wanting our great men to be like us and still be great men. Bronzes must be impenetrable to withstand all the pressure they are exposed to. They are made of special alloy. Someday one of our great men may expose himself. Expose all the doubts and fears and confusions he has locked up inside. We will be terrified.

XIX

CHESTER DANA had the habit of standing long hours in the balcony above the New York Stock Exchange during his apprentice days as a financier. I was impelled to try it myself, peering down on this market place which has changed very little in physical appearance since Dana's time. I watched with fascination and horror the vast human pit constantly in movement, like a living organism, pulsating, churning to a heartbeat of its own. The prim voice of a female guide attempted to explain to untutored visitors what was happening below as telephone clerks rushed orders to the traders who in turn gathered in little clusters at the trading posts. For me it was a confusing spectacle— confusing and revolting. I could not help feeling that the economic life of a great nation should move with more dignity, more sense of order and solemnity. This hurly-burly of little men running to and fro seemed so demeaning. So chaotic. If the stock market, as Bernard Baruch once wrote, serves as "total barometer for our civilization," heaven help our civilization.

Dana was amused when I mentioned my misgivings to him. "How would you organize it differently?" he asked in his matter-of-fact fashion. I had to confess that it would take wiser brains than mine, but surely our economic commerce could be managed in a better way. He cut me off. "The Soviets have a different way of handling it, but I doubt if it is better." I was stung by the suggestion that I might favor a totalitarian alternative but Dana appeared not to notice. "What you must remember is that the stock market is a pretty accurate mirror of people—people trying to anticipate what the future holds. It reflects their hopes and fears, their ambition and their greed. And it conducts its business out in the open so that no small group of men can get away with running things for their own selfish purposes—not for very long."

I was tempted to retort that Dana could afford to be sanguine about the stock exchange. It had been good to him. Within a remarkably few years, it made him a wealthy man. Chester Dana was one of that strange breed who amassed financial power even though they "organized no corporations, created no factories, built no railroads." And he accomplished this feat without ever having to sully himself with the sweaty business on the floor of the stock exchange. Dana, in fact, never owned a seat on the exchange, never once went down from the balcony onto the floor. Rare among the speculators, he didn't even keep a ticker in his office.

My own prejudices had undoubtedly been helped along by Henry Adams' description of the notorious speculator Jay Gould: "He was a broker, and a broker is almost by nature a gambler. . . . His nature suggested survival from

161

the family of spiders: he spun webs, in corners and in the dark. His disposition to subtlety and elaboration of intrigue was irresistible. He had not a conception of a moral principle."

Dana's admirers from his Wall Street days would quibble with my use of the word *speculator*. One of them assured me, "In strict point of fact, he did not speculate in the fashion of those who rode the daily ups and downs of the market. He never tried to establish a corner on a particular stock so that he could make a killing. He was a shrewd investor and one of the early pioneers of that useful practice known as 'investment counseling.' "

Right from the outset, according to those who watched his rise, Dana never put a foot down wrong. He served a notably brief apprenticeship in the investment section of Brown Brothers. "Dozens of bright young Ivy Leaguers disappear into those back rooms every year. Some drop by the wayside, some spend decades fighting their way to the top of the bank. But not Dana. He was a loner and as soon as he learned the ropes he was ready to strike out on his own." This came from J. D. Suffrage, a trader several years his senior with whom Dana afterward shared offices though nothing so formal as a partnership. Before too long, several investors of considerable means had retained Dana to handle their portfolios.

How did he succeed so surely while others failed? I got various answers to this query as often as I put the question. Old Suffrage, who fancied himself a student of history, pulled down a vellum-bound copy of Napoleon's memoirs from his library shelves and dug out the quotation: "There is a gift of being able to see at a glance what prospects are offered by the terrain. . . . One can call it the *'coup d'œil militaire,'* and it is a gift which is born in great generals." The terrain was favorable to daring initiatives by a newcomer when Dana entered the financial world. This was the onset of the longest bull market in history. Everything—or almost everything—was rising with the tide of prosperity, J. D. Suffrage told me. "But you must realize that nobody *knew* it was going to be the longest bull market. A lot of veteran speculators were jumping in and out, hedging their bets, selling short as often as they sold long, and behaving all the time as though they expected everything to come tumbling down. I can name you some of the smartest men in the game who made and lost substantial fortunes during that bull market. Too smart for their own good. And I can name you others who got so used to riding prosperity that they failed to jump clear when the great crash came. But Dana rode and Dana jumped just at the right time."

As I moved around the investment community picking up nuggets of Dana lore, I discovered that his success story was as fascinating to the professionals as it was to me. Busy men would drop everything to spend the afternoon reminiscing about his mysterious ascent. Two brokers who had handled transactions for him joined me for an evening in the splendid high-ceilinged dining room of New York's University Club. Before long, they were contending with each other about the "essential" qualities that made Dana a success.

One broker put the emphasis on brains and hard work. "In those days, we didn't have the economic indicators we have today. Each man had to develop his own intelligence system to tell him what was going on. It was hard work and

163

I happen to know that Dana spent long hours and did a good deal of traveling to gather the facts he needed before making his decisions. He had amazing powers of concentration and he concentrated on the basic industries. Take sulphur, for example. It's a bellwether commodity because it supplies steel and all the other basic industries. I watched Dana move into sulphur in a big way. Then he moved right out when the facts showed him that the market was shaky. I always thought Dana was one of the first of the real market analysts—operating on the basis of knowledge and not just on hunch."

The other broker wasn't convinced this told the whole story. "None of us know for sure how Dana operated. He never bothered to explain why he was doing what he was doing or, as a matter of fact, who he was doing it with. But nobody ever got very far in Wall Street operating on facts alone. That's why lawyers always make such bum traders. Before they get all their facts together, the market has passed them by. Men like Dana have to have powerful intuitions. They gather all the evidence they can but then they rely on instinct to tell them when to act and how to act. A good trader has got to be a loner. He entertains no illusions and he recognizes no alliances. And, above everything else, he's got to have nerve."

Try as I might, it was impossible to dredge up an unfavorable word about Dana among his contemporaries on Wall Street. Time seemed to add a patina of admiration for this young man who moved quietly about his business, never hurried, unfailingly courteous, unaffected by the pressures that turn so many traders into nervous wrecks. On one thing everyone agreed. Dana was a private man. He kept

164

his counsel and made his moves without bothering to justify them. Like other skilled traders, he carried on dealings through a variety of brokers so that no one knew their size and scope, even knew for sure whether he was moving in or out of the market on a particular stock. Suffrage, though sharing offices for more than a decade, confessed admiringly that he was ignorant of Dana's dealings most of the time. When, on rare occasions, Dana joined the after-hours sociability at the old Waldorf Hotel, a favorite gathering place of the insiders, it was observed that he did more listening than talking.

"He never said it in so many words, but I got the impression that he disapproved of a great deal that was happening in those days," Suffrage told me. "Dana never enjoyed the battles of the bulls and the bears. One time I went to him with a red-hot tip about a combine getting together in copper. He wouldn't touch it."

When did Dana first feel the telltale tremors that signaled the approaching disaster of 1929? A favorite form of reminiscence on Wall Street is to recount the tales of how each celebrated operator met this crisis. How Jesse L. Livermore, one of the biggest bulls of all time, suddenly became a bear little more than a month before Black Thursday. How Benjamin Block was traveling in England that summer when, with sudden premonition, he hurried back and unloaded his entire holdings before the crash. How Bernard Baruch managed to convert a large share of his assets into dollars and gold.

Young Chester Dana was not yet in their league, but he read the warnings as early as any. More than a year before, he had gradually phased out his management of other

165

investors' portfolios, advising each to keep a liquid position. When the debacle came, his own account was in cash or securities calculated to weather a long storm. "He not only survived the crash in good shape but he had the sense to hold out the next year when a good many speculators came rushing back into the market," J. D. Suffrage told me. "He came through that crisis unscarred. Then when the market had really bottomed out, he began picking up blue-chip securities that had nowhere to go but up. Bought 'em and held 'em. Still holds them so far as I know. One of the few traders I know who made money out of the Depression."

When I attempted to probe Dana on the period of the great stock market crash, he voiced impatience with the legend of his psychic powers. "There was no reading of sheep entrails on my part," he commented drily. He told me that Baruch had once given him a book entitled *Extraordinary Popular Delusions and the Madness of Crowds,* a historical account of mass hysteria over the centuries. It had had an enormous influence on his thinking. "I reached the conclusion sometime in 1928 that we were headed for another period of mass hysteria. Events bore me out."

As I tried to recreate the horror of that period, I could not help recalling Joseph Conrad's saga *Lord Jim,* about the first mate who abandoned his stricken ship and spent the rest of his life trying to recapture his lost honor. Only there were differences in Dana's saga. The schooner in Conrad's tale survived its mishaps, but the great vessel of Wall Street did sink, carrying down millions of helpless passengers. And, second, there was no dishonor for those mates in the stock exchange who jumped clear. Not dis-

166

honor but admiration and envy for men like Dana who had the cunning to survive.

It is, I know, a false analogy. Wall Street must operate on a different code of survival. I have read the marvelous rationalizations of how even the bears, who make their profits on market failures, are performing a valuable role. They help to keep the market honest. No one can criticize a trader for selling short, much less for simply liquidating his holdings as Dana did.

What could Dana, or a dozen Danas, have done to prevent the disaster? The age was past when a single tycoon like J. P. Morgan could stand up and quell the hysterics of the market place. Wall Street had become too big, too diversified, too leaderless. So the only alternative was to take to the lifeboats. And Dana apparently never flinched as he silently abandoned ship, knowing that even to sound an alarm might help precipitate disaster.

My populist upbringing is clearly revealing itself, but I like to think that my reservations about Wall Street go beyond provincial prejudice. I despise the dehumanization of the system. Of course, the traders can be just as kind as you and me, go to church on Sunday, display sweet charity to the needy. But standing in the New York Stock Exchange balcony and peering down, I felt that those men below had been reduced to cogs in a perpetual-motion machine. A computer could do their work better than the clerks and traders scurrying around the floor. I compared this scene with the one from the Senate gallery. The Senators, despite all their drolleries, their clasping of hands and pawing of shoulders, despite the never-ending oratory, represent mankind at work. A single man can affect the course of human events in that forum. Even the House of Representatives, despite its confusion, gives the feeling that human reason may occasionally have a role to play.

But I failed to find the role for human reason on the floor of the stock exchange. It looked like a forum fiendishly designed to create "extraordinary popular delusions and the madness of crowds." The stock market, I concluded, stimulates and enlarges the public hysteria. In good times, it nurtures man's worst instincts to make a killing— to get rich quick. In bad times, even the most idle rumor can send it into spasms of despair. Surely, the economic muscles of a strong and virile nation ought to be governed by a nervous system superior to this one.

Did Chester Dana ever share any of these misgivings? It would be contrary to the habits of a lifetime for him to voice them even if he did. But there is evidence that the experience of 1929 and the ensuing depression years left a mark on Dana. I got a clue to this while probing the reasons why during the mid-thirties he and old Suffrage came to a parting of the ways. After more than a decade together, each moved into separate quarters. Other Wall Streeters had wondered about the reason for the split.

J. D., a rolypoly little man full of life's juices, loved to talk and invited me to the comfortable but hardly sumptuous uptown apartment where he and his wife lived in semi-retirement. While he had survived many ups and downs during his time on Wall Street, he had obviously not enjoyed the same financial rewards as Dana.

Not the faintest tint of bitterness colored his references to his former colleague. As discreetly as I knew how, I raised the question of why they had chosen to end their quasi-partnership. He took no offense but answered forthrightly: "Two schools of thought began to form in the financial community during the nineteen-twenties and to develop during the thirties. One school I like to call the Yankee trader tradition. The other school was influenced by European notions. The Yankee school believed in free enterprise. The continental school turned more and more to government as a way of manipulating the economy. I belonged and still belong to the Yankee school. Dana, especially as the great depression wore on, started looking toward Washington for the cure."

As old J. D. talked, I realized with a shock what an unreconstructed reactionary he really was. This chipper little man, with alert brown eyes, did not rant and rave about the destruction of capitalism by the socialist bureaucrats in Washington. But he was vehemently opposed to every governmental reform since Carter Glass fathered the Federal Reserve System to bring order to the banking community. "In theory, it sounds fine for the Fed to manage the supply of currency. But in practice, no government agency has the nerve to tighten up on money enough to prevent inflation." He had as little faith in the other devices for regulating the · economy. Not that he favored boom and bust. He simply didn't think there was any better way than a free market for preserving a dynamic system. A little trust-busting, he argued, was about as far as government ought to go.

But Chester Dana had not retained, if he ever held, this pristine faith in free enterprise. Old J. D. believed Dana had been attracted by some of the notions of John Maynard Keynes. "Lord Keynes," Suffrage came close to spitting out his name, "put together a theory that encouraged

169

government to move whole hog toward the regulated economy." That was when Suffrage and Dana decided it would be wise to have an amicable divorce. Their paths had not crossed since, though J. D. assured me he held nothing but the friendliest feelings toward his erstwhile office mate. "We just didn't see things the same way," he remarked wistfully. "There were these two schools of thought."

I came away with a new appreciation of the struggle that not only pitted class against class but partner against partner. Here in New York, which had so long ruled the nation's economy, men looked with totally different eyes at the shift of power toward the nation's political capital two hundred miles away. Many, like J. D. Suffrage, would live out their lives protesting the shift. Some shared the terrible pessimism of Henry Adams when he wrote more than a half-century earlier, "The national government, in order to deal with the corporations, must assume powers refused to it by its fundamental law,—and even then is exposed to the chance of forming an absolute central government . . . which sooner or later is likely to fall into the hands it is struggling to escape."

But others reconciled themselves to the shift of power and the new role of government. There is no evidence that Chester Dana took a lead position in this school of thought. He kept about his business during the thirties. He once told me that he had voted for FDR in 1932 and, again "with certain misgivings" in 1936. By the time the elections of 1940 came round, war had started and Dana was already in Washington.

Did Dana's experience on Wall Street leave him, like Jay Gould, without a conception of moral principle? No, I do not think so. All his later life proved him to be a highly moral man. But did he really like his life on Wall Street? I asked him this question. He thought a long time before answering. "I liked what it taught me," he said. "But I never particularly liked making money or helping others grow rich. I was ready to leave long before the opportunity came my way."

XX

December 3, A.D. 2

A former President died today and the nation prepares to engage in mourning. It will not be in the sobbing, convulsive fashion of the Italians or the breast-beating, clothes-rending style of the Greeks. Still it will be genuine as plain, God-fearing people line the streets and sadly stare the hero onward to his final resting place.

Who are the mourners and where were they when the hero lived? Henry Mann, having long studied the people's attitude toward their Presidents, has devised a theorem: the degree to which an incumbent President is believed capable of evil is in direct ratio to the believer's distance from the White House. He has tested this theorem and, allowing for certain variations, finds it to be true. Of course, a believer's distance from the White House cannot be measured in geographic miles since some are quite distant

172

who live nearby. "But time and again," Mann re-marks, "the President who takes an occasional highball has become an habitual drunkard by the time his story reaches Boston. If he has an eye for ladies, the people in Lake Forest, Illinois, believe him to be a sex maniac."

Are the people who accept the most pernicious rumors about their President the same ones who line the streets when death claims him? Or do we have two cults of citizenry, the haters and the mourners? Mann doubts the latter, for he believes people are capable of monumental inconsistency. B himself has felt contrary sentiments toward Presidents and today he, too, thinks sad thoughts about the passing of this leader whose public service he never much admired. Democracy promotes so few to the ranks of genuine heroes, requiring for the most part great wars, decisively won, to raise a new crop. Always when one is gone, there is a feeling of waste because his talents were not more fully recognized, of neglect because nobody told him how much he was loved.

If the people are capable of such inconsistency toward their heroes, B wonders what must be the hero's attitude toward the people. He tries to put himself within the hero's skin. He feels the shiver of apprehension when destiny marks a man to move separately from the pack. Or does a hero shiver? Does he feel fear or exultation when he wins the first plaudits from the crowds and finds himself consigned to the corridor of leadership?

Try as he may, B cannot put himself in a President's skin. He has read all he can about this peculiar kind of hero who embodies the love-hate sentiments of a nation. He knows that Presidents habitually talk of the inspiration they derive from "the People." Watching them, he is struck by a sense of mystery at their compulsion to touch and be touched by the crowds, so different from the way leaders behave in any other nation. Is it merely ego gratification that causes a President of the United States to dart free from his guards to be pawed and pounded, cuffs ripped and hands bleeding in this unholy communion rite?

B knows enough about Presidents to be convinced that they are shrewd and self-serving men. Surely in the long ascent to power they have grown skilled in the study of other men's faces, quick to detect the cunning most men exhibit when they have intimate dealings with their leader. Perhaps that is why Presidents prefer the raw, undiluted emotions they behold in people in the mass.

Perhaps there are other motivations. In the lonely eminence of the White House, how does a President develop ways of measuring his leadership? He reads the daily harangue of the editors and columnists; he studies the ridiculously precise barometer of the pollsters; he hears the unending diatribe of the Congress. But how does he really know what the great god Public is thinking and feeling and judging? So he goes to the fickle god and tries to make his own measurements. And surely, in his heart of hearts, he must realize that this, too, is a meaningless measure. Not till he is long dead, not till the screamers and the mourners have left the scene, will there be the real measuring and the lasting judgment of his greatness.

XXI

ONCE I made a summer's journey to Mexico and there attended a bullfight. After the first kill I left, having grown nauseated during the prolonged sadism. I recalled the scene often during my second spring in Washington when we were witnessing the undoing of the President. Like a ferocious bull at bay, the nation's leader was still going through the motions of leadership, making frantic efforts to seize the initiative and turn on his pursuers, trying to display the vigor of his more golden time. But too many banderillas has been shoved into his neck muscles. Paralysis had set in.

Weekly, the polls showed he had sunk to new depths of public disfavor. It was the signal every politician was waiting for. To the cries of the opposition in Congress were now added wails from the President's own supporters. Young ones, still uninitiated in the ways of power, did not hesitate to rise and add their protest. Men long loyal to the President had grown silent. From his inner councils came repeated tales of intrigue. A story made the rounds attribut-

176

ing to the President the philosophical utterance: "It's like it always was. If you are not doing it to them, they are doing it to you."

Washington had become a city of rumor as each ambitious contender sought to get his story before the public. Secretary Dawson, always a maverick, had declared open warfare on his own administration. When he came to the Dana home one evening, he supplied the guests with an inside account of the growing disarray, how the last Cabinet meeting heard an angry harangue by the President on the meaning of loyalty, how Cabinet members were openly snubbing one another, how Dawson himself was tempted to submit his resignation and carry his grievances to "the people."

Nothing the President attempted to do seemed to work any more. He had appointed a prestigious commission of public-spirited men who were charged with making a far-reaching survey of the country's ills and presenting a concrete blueprint for setting things right. Evidently the President had not reckoned on their disillusionment, for their report proved to be a blistering indictment of his leadership. On Capitol Hill, countless new investigations had sprung into existence, vying with one another to snare choice witnesses and produce daily sensations for the press. Sensations were not hard to come by, for the lesser bureaucrats had also got the message and were busy with their own intrigues. And beyond the firecracker bursts of petty scandal, there were daily rumblings about corruption yet unexploded which, some said, would rock the capital if the fuses were ever lit.

As I watched this sad spectacle, I was impressed how

177

much government in Washington is held together by faith—faith that a single man can stay on top and make the system work. But it is shallow faith. I held no brief for this particular President. Still I felt the familiar nausea while watching the savagery of those who sought to bring him down. I began to wonder whether there might not be a more humane method of deposing leaders.

I watched carefully for Dana's attitude toward the mounting crimination. After all, he had parted with the President himself. Yet amid all the abuse that filled the papers and infiltrated the Dana salon, I do not recall one expression of "me-tooism" from this solitary man. Pain seems the best word to describe Dana's attitude—pain and silence. On occasion, he would break the silence. When Professor Alton Sharp, Dame Dana's friend, made a caustic argument that the President's Far East policy offended the consciences of "decent" men, Dana's patience was stretched too far. "It may offend their consciences but it does not improve their memories," he replied. "Our Far East policy represents the accumulation of many misjudgments. It had a thousand architects and a good many thousand artisans."

Sharp somewhat unctuously replied that he was glad that he could claim no credit as architect or artisan for this "catastrophe." "Perhaps you are fortunate. Perhaps not," Dana observed mildly. When the Professor tried to make amends by remarking that Dana at least had the good sense to "disassociate" himself from the President, the old man cut him off abruptly. "It's too bad that the President does not have the luxury of disassociating himself from catastrophe."

As the rebellion grew, Dana grew more silent, more

178

pained. Hardly a week passed without a new magazine article, a new book of revelations. Dana would shake his head. Only once did he open up to me. A former official had published a book which was being hailed as "brilliant" confirmation of the fact that the President failed to heed the "clear warnings" of his subordinates that his policy was headed for disaster. "It is remarkable how clear a man's recollections can be when his misgivings are subsequently proven right," Dana said sadly. "It may be that every word in that analysis is God's truth. It still doesn't answer the question: At what point does a President cut his losses? If he guesses wrong, he is in trouble no matter which way he decides. There would be just as many advisers recollecting how they had given him fair warning to stand firm."

I thought I detected, way down deep, lingering affection for the President on Dana's part. Or maybe it was a love-hate feeling somewhat akin to what I myself was feeling toward Dana. He never mentioned the leader he had once served so intimately. He resisted my efforts to draw him out on the more personal side of their relationship. But I could tell—or thought I could—that his sympathies still lay with the man undergoing so much vilification. It was a passive sympathy. Dana must have concluded that the tide of hostile opinion was too strong to be turned by cautionary words—that the only course for sober, sensitive men was to grow silent.

XXII

SOMEBODY ought to do a study on what war—large, holy war, that is—means for leadership in a democracy. We know that most of our "great" Presidents happened to be war Presidents. In time of holy wars, we create and celebrate leaders; in time of peace or small, pesky wars, we devour them.

You could certainly build a case by listing those who moved into leadership when they rushed to serve their country during the Second World War. Chester Dana was one. If it were possible to orchestrate the life of this man in the manner of a symphony, surely this would be the movement when all his themes achieved a splendid unity. He had long been ready. But, except for war, would he have ever sought or been summoned? War provided the excuse to uproot children, accept cramped living quarters, make all the adjustments that in peacetime are simply too troublesome to bother with.

Dana legend, as I have mentioned, claims that he foresaw the approach of war in a single revelation, after con-

180

versing with a Jewish refugee from Nazi Germany. The reality is less dramatic. For some years Dana had been a conscientious member of the Council on Foreign Relations in New York, attending the endless series of lectures and seminars, rubbing shoulders with others who composed that group which more recently has been called "the Establishment." Nothing was prearranged or preordained about his participation. Nobody singled him out for membership in the Establishment. It happened to suit his interests to keep abreast of foreign affairs and he relished this association with other Council members. When FDR, in a master stroke, called old Henry Stimson back to the colors as Secretary of War, the net was thrown out for those who could fill key positions in the Secretary's office. Dana had met Stimson once or twice at Council meetings. His name was put forward by a friend of a trusted friend of the venerable statesman. Someone was needed in the Secretary's office who had a good "overview" of the nation's industry. By such chance, a man's career can take a major turn.

It is a fact, Dana admitted to me, that he became convinced war was on the way after hearing a distinguished scholar, a Jewish refugee from Germany, address the Council. The man's speech made him aware of the growing hysteria in Germany. He recalled that the scholar stated the proposition that "In times of great national trial and excitement so many men go mad that madness becomes a sort of epidemic." But it was only one incident in an accumulating body of evidence that convinced him that World War II was on its way.

This time, the course for Dana was not to retire as he did before the hysteria of 1929. Instead he became one of the

181

early interventionists and, from the time of the Nazi take-over of Czechoslovakia, he was convinced that America must inevitably enter the war. Typically, his was a quiet decision but nonetheless resolute. He was more than ready to leave Wall Street and accept the call to Washington in the summer of 1940.

It was a vastly different capital city in those days, still hardly more than a Southern village despite the invasion of New Deal bureaucrats. Negroes rode in the back of street-cars and did not dare to enter white restaurants. Chevy Chase and Silver Spring were distant suburbs, not yet part of the metropolitan sprawl. Across the river, Virginia was largely unbroken countryside with the Pentagon building still on the drawing boards. Housing in Washington was becoming scarce, so Dana settled his family in a large, old-fashioned apartment on Connecticut Avenue. Dame Dana made the transition without complaint.

Viewed these many years later, this was a golden time for entering public service. Old Stimson, an austere father figure whose closest associates never called him by his first name, was capable of inspiring intense loyalties. He had an easy manner of command, keeping a respectful distance from details and permitting trusted deputies a wide sphere of discretion. Both he and the Army Chief of Staff, General George C. Marshall, brought grace to the military effort. They helped cushion the rude shock to a nation preparing for war. Immediately around him, Stimson assembled a group whose names have become legendary—Robert Patterson, John McCloy, Robert A. Lovett, Harvey Bundy. When reminiscing, Dana always displayed a glow of warmth for these wartime associates.

This was the right place to be. During peacetime, the Secretary of War was low man in the Cabinet, seldom consulted by the President about anything important. But as the nation reluctantly moved toward war, all this began to change. Stimson and his deputies were party to almost daily White House consultations. The War Department became involved in nearly every sphere of policy, foreign and domestic. A shrewd and able staff man, by guarding his options, could project himself into the vital center of policy making.

Dana showed instant aptitude as a staff man. All his prior experience had helped to sharpen his capacity for this work. He developed a reputation as a troubleshooter, probing into a complex problem without getting bogged down in details, producing a concise report and suggesting a course of action. He had a skill, in one associate's metaphor, for "putting handles on problems." He could lay out a series of intermediate steps by which to move toward ultimate solutions. He adapted himself to the art of thinking for his bosses and preparing memoranda designed for the signature of the Secretary or the President. I have been assured that Dana contributed his share to Rooseveltian rhetoric during those critical years. Above all, he carefully observed the passion for anonymity which is mandatory for good staff men in high government offices.

Being so passionately anonymous, Dana naturally attracted the attention of those who counted. Mr. Stimson developed respect for his abilities and called on him for increasingly responsible tasks. On several occasions, Dana accompanied the Secretary on visits to the White House.

Dana must have sensed the excitement of the place. And he surely treasured these opportunities to observe the man

183

who, along with Churchill, had assumed leadership of the free world. Once he described for me the startling change in this President during the nearly five years he watched him. At first, a cocky, crippled giant with leonine head who tackled his chores with so much zest, so much sheer love of power. Roosevelt's incorrigible meddling always irked the tidy Stimson, but there was deep respect and liking between the two men. Then war had drained Roosevelt's great energy and the steel braces grew heavier till toward the end, as with Moses, his underlings were obliged to hold up his arm so that his reign might continue. It had been terrible, Dana recollected, to watch the burden of the Presidency destroy a strong man. "Anyone who has served a President at close hand," he observed emphatically, "loses any ambition to hold the office himself."

But in the beginning FDR had been full of the joy and cunning of politics. In an election year he had outfoxed the Republicans by bringing two high priests of Republicanism, Stimson and Frank Knox, into his Cabinet. Both knew what the President was doing but came along anyway. Dana attended Stimson's confirmation hearings in the Senate. He described for me how Robert Taft, whose Presidential ambitions had been frustrated for the first time only a few days earlier, mercilessly badgered Stimson for an admission that he sought American involvement in the war.

"But wasn't that in fact Stimson's objective?" I asked.

"I think we knew that America would become involved. But we also knew that Taft was trying to stir up all the ugly fears of isolationism," Dana answered coldly.

That first year the President played a cat-and-mouse game with the isolationists. There was the brilliant initia-

184

tive, purely Rooseveltian, of swapping fifty destroyers to Britain in exchange for naval bases. This was followed by FDR's sponsorship of Lend Lease, which Stimson privately called—and Dana agreed—"a declaration of economic war." But then, fearing a public revolt, Roosevelt drew back. He resisted the urgings of his military advisers to take more aggressive steps against the Nazi naval menace in the North Atlantic. The nation drifted. And Congress, by the frightening majority of only a single vote, made the decision to extend the draft less than four months before Pearl Harbor. Stimson and his men suffered frustrations during that year of indecision. They tested to the limit their capacity to sound the call to arms. Dana himself took to the stump on occasion and followed the Secretary's lead in urging sacrifice in the cause of freedom.

Viewing the scene, I cannot help but marvel at the razor's edge these men—and, indeed, the nation—danced along. Twenty years of irresponsibility—refusing to join the League of Nations or the World Court, holding to a policy of neutrality which forbade America to "consult" with other countries over breaches of peace—had produced deep indifference toward the rest of the world. Now the Nazis were laying siege to Moscow. The threat was coming to our doorstep.

And still our nation was only half awake. Dana told me he often had cause to ponder a remark Stimson had made nine years earlier, when he was Secretary of State, that "The situation in the world seemed like the unfolding of a great Greek tragedy, where we could see the march of events and know what ought to be done, but seemed to be powerless to prevent its marching to its grim conclusion."

185

In July 1941, with disaster looming on every front, Stimson read him a pessimistic excerpt from his diary: "It is a problem whether this country has it in itself to meet such an emergency. Whether we are really powerful enough and sincere enough and devoted enough to meet the Germans is getting to be more and more of a real problem."

Yet, Stimson and his colleagues moved with sure, patient steps to prod and goad the nation into preparation for war. Caught up in a dizzying variety of activities, Dana was, like his Secretary, never rattled, never weary. First came the job of industrial mobilization. A fine political balance had to be struck between the urgent quest to get war production going and the threat of profiteering by war merchants. Dana's experience in reading a company's balance sheet at a glance served him well. He knew how to strike a hard bargain for the War Department without yielding to the anti-business bias of what Stimson wryly called "the New Deal cherubs around the throne." He kept a sharp eye on businessmen who insisted that the consumer needs of the economy still came first.

"I saw him sit down with a group of company executives —electrical manufacturers—and pleasant as you please, without batting an eye, let them know he knew they were cheating on the war effort," Dana's former military aide, Howard Jasper, a rawboned West Pointer, told me. "He didn't bluff or bully. But he got his way."

That same military aide accompanied Dana on a diplomatic mission to shore up the defense of the Panama Canal among neighboring Central American countries. "It was delicate business. Those Latinos were explosive fellows and

Dana hadn't any experience in dealing with them. But I have to hand it to him. He had them eating out of his hand in no time. He created the atmosphere that he trusted them and they trusted him. It worked. The Secretary gave him a citation for that job."

I came close to feeling envy as I traced Dana through these war years. It must have been gratifying to be where the action was, member of a team of outstandingly talented men, testing one's capacity to the limit. Dana was not a man, in Stimson's words, "looking for what the job would do for him." But the job did do things for him nonetheless. For the first time in his career, he was part of a cause much bigger than himself. He was not alone.

There was one episode which points to a side of Dana that I had not fully anticipated. Just after the Normandy landing, Jasper told me, Dana was given a temporary military commission as Colonel; they went to London to review the supply situation for the European invasion. "It was a routine mission but Colonel Dana wasn't satisfied to wind it up and get back to Washington. First thing I knew he had finagled a trip over to inspect General Patton's headquarters in Normandy. Cooked up an excuse that he wanted to see how well the supplies were moving to the forward troops. Well, we visited old Blood and Guts. We toured advance positions where the shooting was not inconsiderable. Chester Dana seemed to get a kick out of being in danger —as though he was testing his reactions under fire."

I thought I knew what Dana was feeling. War passed me by and the closest I ever came to death was my bout with polio. You don't get much chance for testing yourself—

whether you are coward or hero. You always wonder whether in a pinch you might turn and run. Evidently, Dana had to convince himself he wouldn't.

But when I broached the subject with Dana, he assured me there were more practical reasons for the junket. Operation Overlord, carrying the battle directly into north Europe, was the fruition of a hard-fought strategy for the men in the Pentagon. Beginning early in 1942, they had pressed FDR to persuade Churchill of the wisdom of a full-scale invasion across the English Channel. For Dana, as for his superiors in the War Department, the way to kill Hitler was to go for his throat. But Churchill and his advisers, too recently shaken by the Dunkirk retreat, kept cautioning delay in north Europe while pressing for expeditions in Africa and Italy and the Balkans.

"We had our necks stuck way out when Overlord was finally launched," Dana told me. Listening to him, I understood the mounting tension as that June dawn in 1944 approached. What if the armada landing on Omaha Beach had been repulsed? What if the massive array of men and equipment crowded onto the Cotentin Peninsula had failed to break out in the drive toward Paris and Berlin? There was cause for anxiety. The wonder is, in retrospect, how these leaders of unblooded troops kept up their confidence of success. Once Overlord was set in motion, the civilian job in the War Department was mainly to watch and wait. But the doughty Secretary of War, approaching his seventy-seventh birthday, was determined to have his own intelligence directly from the scene. "Mr. Stimson instructed me to make certain that nothing was being spared this enterprise," Dana remembered.

188

Describing that trip, Jasper gave me a sidelight on the early relationship between Dana and Henry Mann. Mann was stationed as war correspondent in London and signed on as a member of the small press group accompanying Dana to Normandy. From Jasper's account, the high-spirited journalist had already developed the affectations that were to become his style of life. "I remember sitting next to him late one night in the bar of a small hotel where we were billeted. The hotel owner broke out some fine old applejack in honor of the occasion and that little fellow got pretty keyed up. He did all the talking, one battle story after another. It sounded like he was covering the whole war single-handed. Colonel Dana just sat there listening and smoking on his pipe. Finally, I figured I'd liven things by kidding Mann about the amount of luggage he had brought along. More bags than the rest of us put together. So I asked him how many changes of underwear he needed for a short expedition like this one. He fixed me with that haughty stare of his—like he was looking down his nose even though he was half a head shorter—and then he says, 'My dear fellow, I'll have you know that I never let anything but silk touch my skin. And it requires at least one change a day.' Godalmighty, the whole table of us nearly broke up laughing. Even Mr. Dana chuckled a few times and rolled his eyes that way he has. Late that night, we had all retired to our rooms when we heard a terrible commotion in the hallway. I rushed out to find Mann standing at one end of the corridor shouting to an orderly at the other end in his high-pitched voice, 'Damn! Damn! Damn! They've put me in a room with someone else and he's not even a member of our press party!' Dana didn't open his door, but next morning he asked me wryly if we had straightened out Mann's lodgings."

"Don't let me give you the wrong impression," Jasper added. "At first, you might think Mann was a silly little bastard. Maybe even a bit fruity. But you'd be wrong. Behind that arty-farty pose he had more brains and gumption than any reporter I ever met. He didn't know the meaning of fear. Mr. Dana saw behind his pose. They developed a genuine admiration for one another on that trip."

Two breeds of businessmen come to serve in Washington. Some who have great reputations back home stay a spell and depart without ever adapting to the place; some even get massacred while never knowing what happened to them. But a second breed, of which Dana was a member, manages to adapt. They recognize right off that Congress is not another board of directors to which the corporation executive merely pays lip service. They learn that no single agent of the government, not even the President, has autonomous power to decide policy. Decision making must be shared. The participant must be skilled in knowing how much to share, how much to hold back.

Dana showed a natural talent for this game despite his many years as a loner on Wall Street. It may be that his Southern origins had something to do with it, especially since many of the committee potentates in Congress come from the South. There is, I am told, a civility among Southerners which natives of other regions rarely manage to imitate. Dana knew all the tactics of courtesy when he was sent to do business on the Hill. Testifying before a committee, he was properly respectful to its members, always eager to provide full explanations, ever solicitous of each member's particular crotchets. But he knew how to stand firm, too, never yielding an inch on his department's position beyond what was prearranged. At times, these relations with Congress are like an elaborate minuet where, amid many bows and curtsies, a gentle dance is carried on. Other times, a witness must show prowess in feint and maneuver.

"So many of those young fellows come up here thinking they're going to teach us how this here government is supposed to work. They're smart as a whip. Know the facts and quick to let you know they know 'em. And you know what happens? They fall right on their ass. Cause we ain't interested in the facts. What we're after is the truth!" This was the testimony to me of an appropriations committee member who recalled Dana's first appearance. Eyes hooded, jowls heavy, he sat behind his massive mahogany desk, twitching from old age and a nervous disease that wracked his body. He wore bright-red bedroom slippers and his office walls were thick with pictures of the great and near-great, each one inscribed with glowing tribute as to one already departed. But his mind was clear and he remembered Dana favorably.

So it was no accident that Dana found himself called on more and more to conduct the War Department's intercourse with Congress. His work with the Truman Committee came to be regarded as the model of effective liaison. He was often invited to join the late-afternoon gatherings behind closed doors. By sharing their bourbon and branch water the senior Senators and Congressmen bestowed on him the final measure of confidence.

191

I may be guilty of painting an overly rosy glow over Dana's period as a wartime activist in Washington. But certainly it must have been an exhilarating experience to share in America's victory over the forces of evil and tyranny. It seems such a far-off time. Giants moved through the streets of Washington in those days. And a whole nation worked as one to create the unity which Dana's boss, Stimson, called the "greatest single moral force with which to crack the enemy's will to resist." How different from the present it appears!

I cannot be certain that it appeared that different at the time, especially to a man with the far vision of Chester Dana. Jasper told me that as the war wore on Dana grew increasingly pensive about the future. "He had put a whole lot of sweat and energy behind the drive for a National Service Act. Figured the only way for the country to avoid the mistakes it made after the First World War was to have universal military training. That way nobody at home or abroad could doubt we meant to keep the peace. But Congress wasn't about to bite the bullet on that one. The NAM and organized labor set up such a howl that the bill never got reported from committee. Dana took it hard."

There were other failures of vision as the war drew toward a close. One that caught my particular interest had to do with the Negro soldier. The Secretary of War had been concerned over discrimination toward those who were serving their country no less valiantly because they were of a different color. It went against his Yankee-lawyer notions of equity. So a working group, with Dana as a member, was set up to bring about racial justice in the service.

For the first time in his life, I believe, Chester Dana

squarely faced the plight of the black man. It seems incredible to me, for he grew up in the same environment I did where the signs of injustice were all around. I remember, almost as vividly as my opening encounter with sex, my first experience with racial prejudice. It happened on a small farm outside town where I used to play as a boy. A prize calf was missing and the county sheriff had been called in to investigate. While a horde of kids looked on, this rednecked oaf singled out the Negro stable hand, our friend, and subjected him to a merciless third degree. Again and again, the poor fellow protested his innocence. In point of fact, the calf had escaped through a hole in the fence and was retrieved not long afterward. But this crude breach of human relations, committed by an official who thought he was doing his duty, lingered like a dirty story in my childhood memory.

Many white Southerners have their first brush with prejudice in similiar fashion. For most, it is a disheartening experience, but they manage to toughen their sensitivities as they grow older. A thousand times I have asked myself whether it would have been any different for me if I had stayed behind to face the daily wear and tear of race relations in a small Southern town.

Evidently, Dana escaped both the crude encounter with prejudice and the wear and tear of growing up to accept it. He approached this task of securing military justice for the Negro with dispassion and—almost—naïveté. Gunnar Myrdal's monumental study on the Negro in American society had recently been published and for Dana it served as a bible. It contained two lessons for him: the first, that discrimination against the Negro did exist as a malignant cancer in the nation; and the second, that the nation should move by orderly stages toward removing discrimination. The obvious first giant step would be to abolish segregation in the service.

It was a disillusioning experience, for Dana soon discovered how deeply embedded prejudice is, North and South. The War Department's working group achieved token victories, which was more than the Navy did, but the Second World War drew to a close with few signs of lasting progress. In postwar America there were even fewer signs that the black man's progress toward equality would move along the orderly path Dana had hoped. There was no sign at all that white Southerners of "good will," like Dana, had a role to play in helping the black man along that path.

"We missed a great opportunity to do swiftly in wartime what is now being done slowly and painfully," Dana told me in a moment of reminiscence. "It could have been so simple. So rational." He waved his hand as if to dismiss the nightmare of the present racial strife.

There was one more nightmare that marked his final days with the military. Dana had not been one of the privileged few who shared the secret of the atomic bomb. But he soon became a leading member of the War Department's civilian staff which gave long and painful thought to the meaning of what happened at Hiroshima and Nagasaki. Dana was quick to perceive that the bomb, despite its temporary payoff, had drastically upset the timetable for building a stable postwar world. History was being hustled. All the well-laid plans to create patient and lasting bonds of friendship with the Soviet Union vanished with the mushroom cloud. Now it was a race with time—nobody realized

194

just how short a time—until the Communists would have their own bomb.

Memoranda from the War Department during this period give a clue to the shattering impact of the bomb. The first hurried reaction was to urge the President to go all-out in bargaining with the Kremlin. We would share our atomic secrets if they would loose the shackles of their police state. Sober second thought soon convinced Stimson and his advisers of the futility of this course. It smacked of blackmail for the U.S., in Stimson's words, to "carry the atom bomb on its hip." So a new War Department memorandum urged that a covenant—U.S.–U.K.–USSR—pledge the three powers to exploit only the peaceful uses of the atom. Dana shared Stimson's impatience that it would take too long to get all the lesser nations on board. The urgent task was to get Joe Stalin on board. But even as Dana and his colleagues were working, events in Eastern Europe gave clear warning that the Kremlin was not prepared to deal in lasting covenants. There was no way to bottle up the genie let loose by the atom bomb.

I have thought that if political scientists were worth their salt, they would concentrate on critical periods such as this one, when history was in flux, to learn useful lessons about human behavior. Why did the men of politics react in precisely opposite ways? What caused a leader like Henry Wallace, from an isolationist farm-belt tradition, to become the fiery prophet of unilateral friendship with the Russians? What motivated others to become apostles of preventive warfare as the only way to deal with the Soviet threat? Surely there must be laws which would enable the political scientist to determine the fissioning of politics as precisely as the physical scientist analyzes nuclear fission. It would be helpful to know these laws.

And it would be helpful to me as the biographer of Chester Dana to know the forces, external and internal, that determined his course during this time of crisis. All I know is the outcome. As the United States moved from the bold self-confidence of World War II into the uneasy frustration of the Cold War, Dana steered his way between the extremes. Perhaps he simply took his guidance from his old boss Stimson, who declared with his usual trenchant eloquence, "In dealing with the Russians, both uncritical trust and unmitigated belligerence are impossible. There is a middle course."

Dana chose the middle course. It was a course that contributed greatly to his role in the years ahead as adviser to Presidents. Yet, for a man with his distant and psychic vision, I also have reason to conclude it was a course that doomed him to periods of agony and doubt.

XXIII

MORE and more that second year conversation in the Dana salon turned to the growing violence in society. My notebook records an evening when Henry Mann, splendid in his embroidered vest and matching pumps, chose this subject to lecture the assembled guests:

> MANN: *"I believe it is possible to discover a natural law governing violence based on precise computations. Such a theory would postulate that violence is the inevitable byproduct of tension. The only thing in the least bit controllable is the manner and the timing.*
>
> *"Any family knows the truth of this law. Tension too long bottled up in the household erupts the more violently when it finally breaks loose. My wife and I come from two different family traditions: the sulkers and the exploders. Her habit was always to retire when angry while mine was to let loose the pressures before they grew destructive. Fortunately,*

197

our marriage was preserved when she came over to my tradition."

Mrs. Mann, a handsome if outsized woman, nods patiently. Someone has said that she must have been persuaded in youth that she was utterly lacking in feminine charm. To her intimates, it is a sad misassessment, for she combines a rare mixture of modesty, native intelligence, and great wealth. Prior to Mann, she married in succession two of the ugliest men in the memory of Washington, ugly in the grand manner. Not too long after matrimony both were afflicted with fatal maladies. This naturally provoked speculation in a city where belief in witchcraft lies barely beneath the surface. But life has made Mrs. Mann a compassionate woman. She seeks nothing but affection and, consequently, is highly thought of.

Her husband picks up his theme. "No people have embraced a philosophy of nonviolence more ardently than those on the subcontinent of India. Yet, when India and Pakistan finally resorted to partition, the pent-up hatreds caused one of the most terrible bloodbaths in all history.

"I haven't the slightest doubt that the law of violence can be reduced to quantitative measurements —so much tension will produce so much unrest. The job of leadership then becomes not how to bottle up this force but how to dissipate it in the least harmful ways."

Old Senator Vale, ever the idealist, is offended

198

by this mechanistic view of history. He chides Mann that it makes a farce of man's long struggle toward the light. "You might as well argue there is no need to curb the killer instinct since the very act of curbing will only heighten it. But I cannot buy such a sordid interpretation. We must impose wise restraints on our baser natures. This I believe with all my heart. I also believe that civilization will flourish and peace on earth be attained only—to use your phrase—by 'bottling up' the instinct for violence. It is all that separates us from the savage."

"As well bottle up man's instinct for sex," Mann rejoins. "A few saints manage to accomplish that feat, though Lord knows what dreams they must have. But you and I are not capable of such sainthood. We have invented the institution known as marriage in order to channel our sex drives. Admittedly it is a fragile institution. Only read your morning paper and you discover how many a husband risks everything—good name, fortune, and family tranquility—to sleep with a woman next door who looks scarcely different from his wife. But marriage is the way we legitimate the violence of sexual relations. That is why we honor and preserve it—and why we need to invent institutions for legitimating other forms of violence. Mark my word! The explosive energy is there when two people or two nations rub together even as when two sticks rub together to produce fire. Our potential for violence grows by the day as we copulate and swell the

199

world's population. Copulation and communication
—these two forms of violent energy may well be
our undoing."

"Your fine theory does not account for the fact
that most men and women live quiet lives," retorts
the Senator. "They have angers and irritations, yes,
but they manage to live with them. It is not the po-
liceman who curbs violence in most people, nor
keeps them out of each other's beds. Their own
self-restraint does so. You, Mr. Mann, have fash-
ioned your quaint notions on the habits of a distinct
minority."

"And you, Senator, have shaped yours on the
brief history of Anglo-Saxon mores which have pro-
vided a tiny portion of mankind a thin crust of civi-
lization."

Old Senator Vale sneers. "Do you then despise
our Anglo-Saxon tradition?"

"No I don't," replies Mann. "And I would rather
have the system that we have imposed on others,
bad as it is, than the one they would have imposed
on us if they'd had the chance. That's not my point.
My point is that we no longer have the luxury of re-
leasing violence in the good old-fashioned ways. We
are too jammed together on this planet and our
muskets have grown too powerful. We must find new
channels for violence. That is my whole point."

Like so many other conversations in the Dana drawing
room, this one petered out. No one took the initiative to
pick up the theme and drive it to its conclusion. No one

200

asked the logical question of Mann: "But what do we do about the situation now, this very day?" Instead, conversation, like some sort of headless snake, slithered off in other directions. I had the sad feeling that it had become merely a way of passing time for most of those who gathered there.

Where was Dana? He was present, but more and more he seemed a man apart even in his own home. I recall one radiant day that second spring when the three of us—the old man, Dame Dana, and I—made the pilgrimage to Williamsburg, where he was to serve as speaker for the annual "Prelude to Independence." The ceremony was rich in pageantry from the time when this tiny community was center of the Virginia Colony. After watching a company of volunteers parade on Market Square, we rode by horsedrawn carriage to the Capitol where dignitaries gathered in the House of Burgesses.

There, it was easy to run one's mind back two centuries and see a nation in birthing pains. Men could really know one another as they sat cheek by jowl on the narrow benches, firebrand Patrick Henry only a few jowls away from Tory John Randolph. In that chamber, George Washington and Thomas Jefferson started their careers.

So many political confusions must have been absent in those days. No need to strike a balance of ethnic blocs, no open antagonism between white man and black, no organized pressure groups, no "military-industrial complex." Men spoke of liberty and justice; other men knew exactly what they meant. Politicians could be simultaneously democrats and aristocrats without being labeled hypocrites. There was so much boundless optimism for the future.

Yet, given all these advantages, they had failed to reach

201

peaceful consensus. Now, at Williamsburg, we were commemorating the call to arms by which men won violently what they could not achieve by appeal to reason. Neighbor turned against neighbor in a bitter struggle splitting the colonies from the mother country. Was violence necessary? Did the American Revolution, whose rhetoric we celebrate, loose a demon fury, violence exploding into further violence whenever any American feels his rights offended?

I knew that Dana had worked hard on his speech. Standing there in front of the Speaker's chair, he delivered it with cool eloquence, his voice seeming to take on deeper resonance in these Virginia surroundings. One could well imagine this tall, distinguished figure present at that earlier time. Dana's speech was a masterpiece of style and lucidity, causing me to wonder why a man with his flair for polished phrases had not exercised it more regularly. He paid tribute to the historic beginnings we were there in Williamsburg to honor. Then by analogy he brought his listeners to the troubled present times. He painted a picture of crisis no less urgent than the one gripping the colonies. But this time we could not deal with crisis by resort to arms. Instead, he urged that we observe another tradition established by our wise and far-sighted ancestors. In Williamsburg, they had directed their minds and their energies to the task of "building institutions." That, Dana exhorted, must be our central task today: to build institutions capable of preserving order and accommodating change. We must have new institutions to meet the new needs of government. Without this continuing renewal, the efforts of individuals would be fruitless. Even the most well-meaning leaders would be helpless before the growing crisis.

It was an appropriate speech for the occasion, but I came away disappointed. Though Dana conveyed a deep-felt conviction, his words seemed full of generalities. In that quiet hall, the threat of crisis seemed far away and his challenge hardly constituted a concrete plan of action. Why could he not say more?

Afterward, while the dignitaries gathered round to congratulate Dana, I slipped off to view a Colonial Williamsburg film about the long-ago crisis. It portrayed a moving story. John Fry, delegate in the House of Burgesses, is torn between his distaste for hotheads like Patrick Henry and his anger against British misrule. As the crisis mounts, Fry's choice is not an easy one. He is a wealthy, contented man and his only son has reached fighting age. At the drama's climax, Fry stands with his longtime friend, John Randolph, and asks what he plans to do. "I'm leaving for England by the first packet. I'm going home," Randolph says sadly. "I *am* home," answers Fry with equal sadness.

There it was. Faced with the necessity for choice, delegate John Fry pledged himself to the hotheads—to the violence and certain disorder that lay ahead. He made his decision. On the way back to Washington, I kept asking myself what Chester Dana might have done if he had had to choose between two such stark alternatives.

XXIV

DEMAGOGY moved into Washington in many small ways before people gave it a name. New types of operators began to emerge—tougher and more cynical than their predecessors. We noted it when Henry Mann, deadly serious, complained of the stepped-up rivalry in his column business. He felt the competition of one slick purveyor of the "inside know" who, making no effort to fit opinion into any coherent philosophy, launched his daily story like an unguided missile. Given a stray piece of intelligence, the new columnist was apt to shoot off in any direction. His craving was for shock value. Nothing else mattered.

The same thing began to happen in other Washington professions. Older, established lawyers, accustomed to servicing the Congressional committee hearings, found themselves being eased out by a younger breed, skilled at stirring legislative controversy to white heat. A new breed of Congressman, mean and ruthless, was taking front and center stage, pushing even one like Connar into the shadow. A new breed of bureaucrat emerged—smug, facile

204

in keeping open his options until the outcome of the mounting struggle could be predicted.

This was no battle of factions. Men of many different persuasions found themselves dabbling in demagogy, yielding to a general decline of values. Perhaps more ominous than the emergence of the toughs was the spectacle of those who had grown silent. All over Washington one saw men of earned reputation who could no longer find appropriate words to say. This was the struggle of the extremes and the center had yielded.

Dana felt what was happening even before it reached him personally. I had the awful sense that he had expected it for a long time. Privately he deplored the ugly events. In the intimacy of his home, he described them with cutting wit. But at the same time I sensed that he was a stranger to the scene. He reminded me of an exile living in the midst of Washington. One night a retired Supreme Court Justice who had come to dinner made a spirited plea that the center must be made to hold. He offered a vague appeal that prominent men should band together to denounce the excesses. The others heard him sympathetically. But no one volunteered to serve as executive director for this mobilization of the middle. So the subject was dropped. Afterward, Dana remarked with his characteristic irony, "Demagogy has never been fought off by the pensioners from public service."

So it came perhaps inevitably to the Dana household. A young Senator from the corn belt, Ernest Hillings, rose on the Senate floor and announced that Dana had been "intimately associated" with a bigtime contractor named Harvey Owen, who had been bilking the federal government of

205

tens of millions of dollars. Hillings said he did not need to convince his colleagues of the gravity of this charge. It established, he declared, "a daisy chain of relationships that stretches right into the White House itself." Corruption, he alleged, had touched the highest office in the land.

I remember my first incredulity at the far-fetched accusation. Incredulity mingled with a faint shiver of fear and excitement. For I was myself involved. It was I who had brought Harvey Owen into the Dana household. I had arranged his continuing association—not with Chester Dana but with his wife.

In ordinary times, it would have taken no more than ten minutes to answer Senator Hillings. But ten minutes was too long. This was a period when people were expected to spit out their allegiances in ten words or less. "Unless you can answer a charge so that it can be summed up in a single newspaper headline," Dana told me caustically, "you might as well say nothing."

The Senator's charge could not be answered that easily. First of all, my contractor friend may or may not have bilked the government. The final facts on that are still in litigation these many years later. Harvey Owen may be proved guilty someday. He had operated in Washington for a long time, having moved from Dayton, Ohio, while still a young contractor. He was a handsome man whom I took to be in his late forties, with pink cheeks and coal-black eyes, hair graying at the temples, slim, no trace of midriff bulge, a man of Irish blood but diluted and refined. Once the details about him began to appear in the press, I learned that I was wrong on almost every particular. Owen was entirely self-made, born and raised in shanty-Irish poverty. He had never seen the inside of a university, having dropped out of high school in Dayton to start his way in the construction business. His age, as best the press could determine, was nearing the middle sixties.

Owen Enterprises stretched across the country wherever there was large-scale building to be done. Since most such business is involved one way or another with government contracts, I must have supposed that Owen was not a stranger to the world of politics. It turned out that he was involved in a big way, carefully avoiding a partisan label by giving equally generously to Democrats and Republicans alike. But this was an isolated part of his life. In all the times I was with him, I never heard him mention politics, never saw him associate with a politician.

I thought I knew Harvey Owen rather well. Certainly he shared some of his more intimate secrets with me. He was a friend of a friend of Henry Mann and our friendship, I believe, happened purely by chance. The fact that I was a writer, Harvard-educated, seemed attractive to him. He was habitually attracted by those who earned their bread in ways remote from his own. He had an almost childish yearning to be connected with the world of intellect and culture. I cannot believe that this restless, fun-loving man, who seemed to have so much leisure time, deliberately snared me in order to ingratiate himself with the Danas.

Whatever the reason, he first invited me to a Sunday brunch at his bachelor quarters on the Georgetown bluffs overlooking the Potomac. I went back many times, for he was a frequent party giver and had a phobia against solitude. At his home, I discovered an entirely different species of the Washington community. Younger people on the

207

whole, for he loved the young and exuberant. Ballet dancers, would-be novelists, enthusiasts of the Arena Stage and Washington Theater Club. Anyone who had a vague relation to arts and ideas.

I said Owen lived in bachelor quarters. Until the time of his exposure, I assumed he had always been a bachelor. He had, in fact, left a wife behind in Dayton—stolid, moonfaced, as seen in newspaper photographs, content not to follow him to his elegant life in Washington, but, being Catholic, unwilling to grant divorce. They had no children.

Harvey Owen always looked after himself superbly. His modern apartment was furnished in good taste, adorned with the works of his latest artistic friends as well as a valuable collection of erotic Hindu statuary. In his recreation room, he had assembled all the accouterments—punching bag, electric horse, barbells, sauna—of a man with a passion for keeping fit. All around the apartment, one came on symbols of the fastidious male. A high-fidelity music system piped into every room. He had telephones all over the place, including a white wall phone right next to his toilet.

That first Sunday brunch gave me an interesting measure of the man. I went assuming that it was to be a sizable gathering. Not at all. I found Owen with one other guest, a handsome auburn-haired woman who had clearly arrived for the party on the previous evening. She was the wife of a well-known British correspondent in Washington, herself American-born, chic, sophisticated, visibly the product of many years on the psychiatrist couch. What she had learned about herself there evidently inclined her to seek nonchalant liaisons such as this one with Owen. It also made her

208

unashamedly open about her sex life. Her poor husband, it seemed, suffered from a lower abdominal hernia that he was deathly afraid might become strangulated. It had effectively curtailed his slight enthusiasms as lover. So she naturally had to seek other outlet for her sexual energies. Owen seemed not the least perturbed by the notion that his role was determined less by his own charm than by a strangulated hernia.

"Dear George, he's such a coward when it comes to surgery. He's covered a dozen wars at considerable risk of life and limb. Never seemed to mind that. But talk to him about getting his intestines mended and he turns pale!" She gave a sharp snort of laughter.

Did George know that his conjugal limitations were causing her to turn elsewhere? I put that question, trying not to appear priggish.

"Oh, he must suspect. Right now he's off at some political shindig held by the Governors in Denver. He keeps a stiff upper lip, British gentleman fashion. Also keeps a stiff lower abdomen with the aid of a truss. He never asks how I spend my spare time so I know he knows."

As we sat there that Sunday morning in the gay, sunlit apartment, discussing infidelity as normally as we might talk about weather conditions, I found myself lulled into an acceptance of Harvey Owen's way of life. Deep down my Southern fundamentalism was offended. It was sin of a high order according to my upbringing. I sensed even then that Owen was consumingly devoted to his own pleasure. He did not appear particularly selfish in his hedonism. Simply single-minded. At the same time, there was a cheerful,

209

guilt-free spirit about everything he did. And I was mightily attracted. At his apartment I found temporary surcease from frustrations arising in the Dana household.

After the second bloody Mary, I relaxed completely and enjoyed the majestic view of the Potomac while George's wife droned on in monotonous detail about her marital problems. Across the river lay the same Virginia countryside I surveyed during those long towpath walks with Chester Dana. Only here we were higher, insulated by gleaming plate glass from nature's reality. Neither winter nor old age nor premonition of approaching death invaded Owen's cozy lair.

Harvey Owen, I soon learned, was a connoisseur of the physical pleasures. For example, he had sampled surfing beaches all over the world and could describe in precise detail the advantages of one over another. "There's a long barren stretch north of Wainea on Kauai. January's the best month," he would specify. "Water's warm and bubbles like champagne. Those waves start far out and you can ride two hundred yards without a hitch." Owen scorned the use of a board. He was a body surfer. We were trying it one June day, still ahead of the season, at Dewey Beach, Delaware, which he had pronounced best on the East Coast. Patiently, with meticulous detail, Owen showed me how to judge the height and sweep of the wave, how to time my plunge for the precise moment when it began to break, how to kick once and then coast, body rigid, arms straight out, as long as the seizure lasted. Soon I had the knack of it and we rode wave after wave. Like Owen, I found wild excitement in this sport. In the terrible embrace of the wave, a man could feel himself one with nature, surrendering his whole self to be tossed, pounded, swept along by its rage until finally ejaculated upon the beach. There was something deeply sexual about it. Owen recognized this in his forthright way. "It's the next best thing to making love," he laughed as we lay exhausted at the end. "Better in some ways. The ocean's better than a woman."

Later on, I was shocked to learn Owen's true age. Neither skin nor muscle tone betrayed him. Once he took me for a game of paddle ball at the Washington Athletic Club where he played regularly. This first contest was our last, for I was hopelessly outclassed. Afterward, sharing adjoining tables for massage and then dressing in the locker room, I envied him his compact physique. I could understand why women found him attractive in bed.

Owen was unabashedly frank about his conquests. One story he told me lingers in my memory as a latter-day Don Juan escapade. He had gone to New York and late at night was returning to his hotel suite when he noticed that a comely young woman, one of a merry quartet of girls on board the elevator, was eying his room key mischievously. On impulse, he had invited them to his room for a nightcap. They told him they were schoolteachers from North Dakota on vacation. "Would you believe that every one of them slipped back to visit me later during the night, one by one? By morning, I was a totally exhausted man."

It sounded so implausible, but for Harvey Owen, completely possible. Four women in a single night. "Variety," he told me in a solemn moment, "is the only bona fide aphrodisiac." Yet I did not see the pathos at the time. Harvey Owen was for me a romantic figure. He had a droll Irish wit. Every tale was prefaced by "You wouldn't

211

believe what happened." Almost as if he himself couldn't believe his own good fortunes. I wonder now whether he had premonitions of the shame and ridicule later to be heaped on him. If he did, his mask was tight.

For there was one other secret he successfully kept from me. Senator Hillings offered police-blotter proof that on two occasions Owen had been picked up by those zealous pursuers of vice who entrap perverts in the public latrines. Each time he had paid his fine and escaped publicity. But the incriminating evidence was there to add credibility to all the Senator's other charges. It provided the biggest shock of all to me, for I had never detected in Owen the slightest hint of homosexuality. I was astounded that this aging man should have the energy left over for this strange pursuit—that a man could be so obsessed and even his close friends unaware of it.

This is the man I brought into association with Dame Dana. One day he had mentioned to me that he would be willing to give financial support to a committee on the performing arts that the Dame was chairing. When I brought her the glad news, Owen had been swiftly invited to become a committee member. No one bothered to check his pedigree. If this sounds remarkably casual, it is not untypical of philanthropy in Washington. More than one ambitious newcomer to the city has managed to move onto the front page of the society sections simply by purchasing a few tables at the annual Symphony Ball.

Owen joined the Dame's committee and dutifully attended all its meetings at the Dana mansion. I very much doubt that he ever met Chester Dana who meticulously

212

avoided his wife's do-good activities. But it was enough to support the half-truth of Senator Hillings' accusation. Since Dana had long ceased being an intimate in the White House, it still seemed laughable that Hillings should stretch the story to smear the President. Laughable but not answerable. A man less proud than Dana would have found it demeaning to try to explain.

In any event, the capital city was no longer in the mood for lengthy explanations. That was the deadly aspect of demagogy. It was no longer adequate to say that because a man like Dana had spent a considerable portion of his life serving the public trust he did not need to explain to a man like Hillings how a man like Owen happened to visit his home.

This was simply one of a firecracker chain of accusations made during this time in Washington. It didn't really damage Dana. He was wealthy and old and protected. Possibly it helped to make him appear more human, less the mysterious figure of bronze, now that others could discuss his embarrassment over their morning coffee cups. No one publicly joined Hillings' denunciation. The local papers even ran editorials absolving Dana from wrongdoing.

Still the city was thick with suspicions. "These are tricky times, my boy," Henry Mann told me by way of explanation. "The Senator is no fool, and someone high up in the Justice Department is slipping him his material."

"How could he have erred so badly on Dana?" I asked. "Was it intentional error?" Mann replied darkly. "Hillings is not above using blackmail, you know. Taking a swipe at

213

our friend Dana could be a way of warning all the dignified types—the Establishment types—that they'd better stay out of this pissing match."

If this was Hillings' intent, he was successful. All over Washington, men and women were learning to be cautious. While this had no perceptible effect on the Dana guest list, I could detect a marked change in the tone of the conversations. Occasionally, an impulsive female would squeeze Dana's hand in parting as if to convey sympathy that best not be expressed in words. I got the impression that it irked him mightily that others might even think of him as a martyr. He was a sensitive man though he masked it well.

A few stood up. Henry Mann became a thundering giant in his counterattacks on Senator Hillings and all the Senator's dirty crew. He showed no fear when one paper after another dropped his column or else abridged it shamelessly. For the first time, I found myself genuinely admiring this diminutive fellow who meant it when he had declared that free men must be prepared to die bravely. But I was also aware that his efforts were futile. Hillings simply shrugged off what he called the "tantrums of the little Mann," spreading the rumor that he was part of the homosexual round robin in the city. It was untrue but no one knew how to deny it.

Demagogy was a disease in Washington that ran its course without benefit of antibiotics. Not all the blame could be placed on a single villain like Hillings. So many got emotional satisfaction from yielding to the excess of passion or from watching those who yielded. Even the hunted sometimes seemed to join with enthusiasm in this peculiar sport. I know this sounds like cynicism, for un-

214

doubtedly many were badly hurt. But it was Mann himself who pointed out the strange phenomenon. "Some people are accident-prone. Some have a secret death wish. Then why should it be unthinkable that many of demagogy's victims have hoped and planned and, yes, even conspired to achieve their fate?"

Or maybe it meant that demagogy had reached us all. For it had made us all suspicious. It had become the central spectacle in Washington. It had served to divert everyone's attention from the important issues confronting our nation. Not Dana, not even the President was the ultimate loser.

215

XXV

LADY M's nephew, fresh out of Columbia, joined her at the Dana table one evening late that second spring. After dinner, he rushed off to other pursuits but not before leaving the rest of us something to mull over. His thesis: Washington had become the most isolated place in America. The city was totally out of tune with the nation's passions. Clearly, the young man believed himself in close tune with "the people." I recorded in my notebook the resulting discussion of whether Washington was a cloistered city:

> *Lady M taunts the politicians. "You have a congenital disposition to listen to yourselves and pretend you have heard the public oracle," she tells those present.*
>
> *Senator Vale responds mildly that he never misses the opportunity to commune with his constituents.*
>
> *"Yes, and I'll bet you never fail to tell them what you are doing for them. But do you ever listen? Not*

216

just listen to their complaints about farm parity and the rest. Do you listen for the quiet noises of this nation?"

Mann, with his customary self-assurance, suggests that the Washington press corps has better listening habits than the politicians. "Nonsense, Henry! You never listened to anyone in your life," Lady M replies tartly. "Sometimes I think you were the original inventor of radar. The only way you learn things is by waiting for the feedback from your own voice."

The conversation sets everyone to speculating whether Washington really represents the nation. Much has changed, Dana points out, in the years since he left Wall Street to come here. New York no longer claims the primary place it once did. But has Washington taken over? Or has the nation grown more fragmented, more diffused? Dana tells an interesting tale of George Washington's vision for making this Potomac marshland the vital center of his new nation. Washington hoped to link the Potomac by inland waterway to the Mississippi River Valley and thereby cause the country's principal commerce to flow past the nation's capital. He also wished to build a great national university here so that the city would serve as the country's intellectual mecca.

This was an ingenious vision, Dana argues. The flow of commerce would have soon transformed Virginia into an industrial economy, cutting her dependence on the slave-holding South and possibly aborting the Confederacy. But both the canal and

217

the university ventures went bankrupt. When John Quincy Adams, Henry's grandfather, tried to regenerate them, he also failed and was ignominiously turned out of the Presidency by Andrew Jackson. The forces of diversity prevailed; Virginia stayed tied to the slave South. So, Dana concludes, the Civil War became unavoidable.

Lady M has the last word. "That's a sad story, Chester, and so like you to remember it. But I wonder if things are much better all these years later. The politicians are always testing out new appeals for national unity. They try to rally their followers with their fancy slogans: 'To heal and to build' and 'Bring us together.' They finance trips to the moon, hoping these will somehow bring a sense of nationhood. But I doubt whether outer space is going to serve any better than George Washington's inland waterway."

That same evening, Lady M rather upset me. She told me she had known my hero, Henry Adams. She had visited several times in her youth the Adams home on Lafayette Square. She was impressed by how very small he was, how prim and self-solemn. "I didn't like him at all," she said. "He was such a tiny creature trying to be a monument, and he had a squinting mind for all the thinking he did." With her enchanting smile meant to persuade, she tilted her pretty head like a bird and added, "I can't bear people who are eternally sorry for themselves, can you?"

It became important for me to determine more precisely why I did like Henry Adams. Except to his closest friends,

218

he must have been a strange man. He lived a great many years in Washington, son of a Congressman, grandson and great-grandson of Presidents. Yet the itch for public office never seemed to torment him. Unlike Chester Dana, he was not an adviser to the high officials in government though he kept close personal ties with a number of them. He played politics only as a word game in his parlor across the square from the White House. He was a genuine voyeur. One commentator claimed that Henry Adams was the only man in America "who could sit on a fence and watch himself go by." In the flesh, he must have seemed pale to Lady M alongside men of action like Teddy Roosevelt.

While still at Harvard, I was aware that it was no longer the intellectual fashion to make a fuss over Adams. He had become slightly passé. But what I admired about him was his courage in exploring matters of the mind. Though sophisticates belittle this man's search for eternal truths, I found myself agreeing passionately with Adams' thesis that "every man with self-respect enough to become effective . . . has had to account to himself for himself somehow, and to invent a formula of his own for his universe."

Inventing a formula for his universe was enough to occupy Adams' whole lifetime—better spent, in my estimation, then the lifetimes of ten thousand present-day scholars. Adams' theory for charting the course of history may have had flaws. Perhaps it was naïve to try, as he did, to compare Thought moving down through Time with an electric current. But Adams ventured and dared. His metaphors continue to have a kind of poetic truth even if they lack scientific value.

219

I see Adams as one who stood on the sidelines and was nonetheless an adventurer. Adventuring led him to a fatal pessimism toward the end of his life. According to his calculations, man was rapidly bringing Thought to the limit of its possibilities. In 1900, Adams wrote his brother: "All we can say is that at the rate of increase of speed and momentum, as calculated on the last fifty years, the present society must break its damn neck in a definite, but remote, time, not exceeding fifty years more. . . . Either our society must stop or bust . . . I do not myself care which it does. That is the affair of those who are to run it."

Adams was wrong or perhaps his timing may have been off. But I am deeply stirred by the daring prophesy in his last long essay: "If, in the prodigiously rapid vibration of its last phases, Thought should continue to act as the universal solvent . . . and should reduce the forces of the molecule, the atom, and the electron to that costless servitude to which it has reduced the old elements of earth and air, fire and water; if man should continue to set free the infinite forces of nature, and attain the control of cosmic forces on a cosmic scale, the consequences may be as surprising as the change of water to vapor, of the worm to the butterfly, of radium to electrons."

Living in the Washington world of Chester Dana, I sensed all about me the dizzy excitement of politicians, scientists, and military chieftains over what lay ahead if only Thought was nurtured with enough dollars. Government was subsidizing Thought in a massive effort to reduce the atom to servitude. The excitement was indiscriminate: for weapons to pulverize mankind, for medicines to make man's life eternal.

No one in Washington seemed to have premonitions that Thought might be approaching the outer limits of its possibilities. Trying to view this world through Adams' eyes, I kept pondering the age-old question whether man was acting on history or history, mercilessly, irrevocably, acting on man. The thought kept recurring to me that perhaps Adams was right. Perhaps mankind had already entered Thought's last phase without being aware of it: worm turning into butterfly or, perhaps, butterfly back into worm. It was not surprising that the metamorphosis was not recognized. After all, Thought had moved far into the age of Copernicus while most educated people still swore fealty to Ptolemy.

What did Dana think about Thought? When I prodded, I found the old man surprisingly well-read in Adams' theories. He claimed to have a high opinion of Adams. But Dana's habit of detachment was too ingrained to permit spiritual partnership with this wild speculator of an earlier time. "Perhaps it says something of our times that man no longer dares try anything as bold as inventing a formula for the universe," he commented wryly. "We know enough to be aware of how little we know."

I found it hard to comprehend Dana's reluctance. I grew impatient with the man who surely must have felt, as his own life drew toward a close, the need for summing up—a need to discover his own interpretation of history's meaning. Dana had witnessed history at close hand. He had had a chance to observe the play of forces in the White House, where history was being made day in and day out. Why did he now remain so detached?

I could not fault Dana alone. Thought's rapid vibrations

221

were producing shock on shock to the nation's nervous system. Yet, the politicians, who long ago rejected Jehovah's formula for the universe, were showing no great urge to invent a formula of their own. Dana's reluctance was an attitude that appeared to be endemic to the nation's capital. No one seemed to care whether Thought was reaching the limit of its possibilities or that society must stop or bust.

What to conclude? I had only the dismal thought that Henry Adams would have been an even more lonely observer in Washington nowadays than he was in his own time.

XXVI

TO understand Dana at his prime, I felt compelled to pursue my researches into that mysterious breed known as President's men. I meant to examine them in their native habitats, define them according to species, study their survival characteristics, learn all I could that pertained to the success and failure of Chester Dana.

I was determined not to rely on published sources. Yet even this, I recognized, does not guarantee authenticity. Men's memories vary, particularly when their self-esteem is involved. And men have astounding differences in their powers of observation. I found men of the keenest intellect who were valueless in reporting what had gone on. Others were color-blind to the subtle shadings of an episode. Still others regarded history as a closed book not to be cracked by an outsider.

One block west and north from the White House stands the Metropolitan Club. In its dining and drinking rooms, one has the impression of looking at power in Washington as at a cross section sliced from a great old oak tree. Gathered there of an average day are concentric circles of President's men dating at least to Harding's time. Contemporary ones hurry in for a pressured lunch, breathing self-importance by the very briskness of their movements. Earlier generations are apt to linger over a second or third martini. One ex-President's man, pointed out to me, always wears a fresh rose in his lapel. He and others who have shared that role have a common nostalgia. Life, I was told, would be downhill for them most of the way on out.

My quest took me many places and I met various kinds of men. I called on Rogers Clark, the longtime Washington lawyer, in his penthouse office atop one of Washington's splendidly antiseptic new office buildings. There, in bizarre contrast to the building's modernity, his suite was furnished in chintzy early American decor. His work table occupied only a tiny corner of the vast room and a single old-fashioned telephone handled his traffic with the outside world. From press clippings, I knew that great corporations compete to buy the fraction of Clark's time not consumed by voluntary service to the President. Yet during my visit nothing was allowed to disturb the tranquility. He preserved an atmosphere of gracious, old-fashioned charm. This tall, handsome man in his box-shouldered suits offered an unflappability that a President, it is said, likes to have around him during a crisis. As I prepared to depart, he took me over to the window and drew the curtain to reveal his magnificent view looking *down* on the White House.

Composure, I soon learned, is only one of the characteristics of President's men. Quite a different species was represented by Robert Badlos, whom I found in the book-strewn study of his little home across the river in Arlington.

224

Badlos, a disheveled, sour-complexioned young man, had served on the payroll of more than one President and nobody knows how many Presidential aspirants. He was the opposite of Rogers Clark, high-strung, full of conceit, impetuous, condescending. Then what explained his popularity with men in high places?

"As a rule politicians are not innovative thinkers," I was told by a White House insider. "This may be good or bad, but it is so. Something about their routine kills the impulse to be creative. But if they are good politicians—ambitious politicians—they recognize the importance of ideas. They are hungry for them—not ideas in the abstract but ideas with muscle in them, ideas they can take hold of. Ideas they can do something with and that will do something for them. Now Presidents are the biggest consumers of ideas in the business. They are like bottomless jugs needing a constant supply of fresh ideas. They need whole teams of bucket boys to service them."

Badlos, I learned, had a further gift. He served the President's need to speak persuasively and in his own distinctive style. So much of the material drafted for his utterance by the bureaucrats fails on both counts. But this ghostwriter was said to have an uncanny genius for adapting himself to a President's idiom. He appeared to be utterly indiscriminate and there were rumors that he often met himself coming and going in rhetoric for his various employers.

Still another species was represented by J. B. Calmoy, not yet turned thirty, who enjoyed celebrity around town as the aide "closest" to the President. Calmoy had reportedly forsaken wife and infant children to be at the President's side when he rose each morning and went to bed each

225

night. His influence went beyond that of a faithful valet. He was believed to be skilled in tugging at the President's sleeve at precisely the proper moment to urge or alter a decision. My strongest impression of this young man was of his boyish lack of guile. He spoke with such becoming modesty. Not until I tried to reconstruct our conversation afterward did I realize that his great candor had revealed nothing very significant. I could understand why a President would want him as a spokesman. Calmoy's appearance of innocence helped allay public fears of something sinister at the power summit. Yet this guileless fellow could walk along tricky paths for the President without making a misstep.

Mr. Composure, Mr. Eloquence, Mr. Guileless—the qualities of President's men read like a cast from a latter-day *Pilgrim's Progress*. Still one more needed to be added: Mr. Loyalty. I discovered him in the person of Rawlings Tarver, a man whose gifts at first acquaintance were not obvious. But he was said to have a capacity for bestowing the one talent which a President values above all others. Loyalty not to the nation, not to the government, not even to the office—but unquestioning loyalty to the man who sits in that office. Tarver's eyes were hard even when he was smiling. He told me he could judge someone at a single glance—whether he was the President's friend or foe. The first and, indeed, the most important thing he wanted to know about a man conducting the President's business: was he loyal? If a man had to have that word defined for him, better look out!

These were not the only species of President's men I came across, but they were the big four. The President's of-

226

fice had grown into a bureaucracy teeming with experts who held titles and offered advice of a variety unknown in Franklin Roosevelt's time. But, at its core, not that much was changed. The Presidency was still the lonely desk of a solitary man in the White House. His essential job was to go on trying to reduce the complexity of government into human terms, assisted by a trusted few.

I found an unexpectedly rich source. There was one insider, David Pearson, who had never committed a word to print, never, so far as I know, put pen to paper. But he had a poet's eye for the detail that illumines history. He told me, for example, of a crisis in the Mediterranean which erupted, as usual, in the dawn hours. A hurried conference at the President's bedside. As Dana offered his assessment, standing nearby the recumbent Commander-in-Chief, a note was slipped to him by the Secretary of Defense. "Your fly is open." Without blinking or faltering, Dana zippered up his trousers and continued his argument. Afterward, the President gravely thanked him for putting first things first in this hour of need.

We were sitting in the aide's small second-story office in the West Wing of the White House. Outside, two secretaries kept up a steady pounding on their typewriters as reminder that the work did not pause for reflective conversations. I could see the unceasing blink of lights on the telephone console. But the aide, a lanky young man with the traces of an untamed cowlick, was intrigued with his subject. "You've got to understand one thing about life around here before you can make sense of anything else. Only one thing really counts. It doesn't matter what your title is or how big you were before. What counts is whether you've got the

227

boss's confidence and how much. The guys in the press are always trying to work out yardsticks. They measure how far your office is from the President's. How big it is. They count how many times a day you see the boss. That's all crap. Usually by the time the reporters figure out who is number one he's already passed his peak."

How did one prepare to be a President's man? The simple answer was that there were no training courses. It didn't help to be an old crony, or a party henchman, or even a born leader. You had to put yourself through a do-it-yourself training course. Pearson told me, "It takes a capacity to think for the President without succumbing to the arrogant notion you *are* the President."

Pearson professed himself constantly mystified by how other men behaved in the President's presence. "Old Charlie Tyson has a reputation as the iron man in the automobile industry. He can fire a plant manager or bully a union leader without blinking his eyes. But let him walk into that Oval Office and he begins trembling like a man with palsy. Something about the aura of the Presidency undoes him. It reduces his utility."

Most would-be advisers, I was told, suffer the opposite curse. "You can see them puffing themselves up when they come in. Trying to get in the right phrase so they can go out afterward and tell their friends how smart they've been. There is this one fellow, a distinguished educator. Knows a lot about scientific matters that the boss needs to know. But he is always wanting to talk about the 'politics' of an issue. 'Mr. President,' he'll say, 'the people will support you if you do thus and so.' Hell, the boss knows all about the politics.

228

What he wants from that fellow is the substance—whether it is the *right* thing to do."

What was the President looking for when he called a man into his office for advice and counsel? "First of all, he wants a man who stays true to himself when he goes in there. But he also wants that man to understand the President's predicament without having it spelled out in detail. He wants a man who can anticipate." Pearson grew thoughtful. "One other thing. You have to draw a fine line of respect for the office. Of course, you don't need to go as far as one of the boss's old friends who always addresses him in the third person. 'Does the President feel well today?' That's gilding the lily. But you can get too familiar too. There's one fellow who knew the boss way back when. He keeps switching back and forth, 'Mr. President' one minute and first-naming him the next. It irks hell out of the boss. I don't think he cares much about the protocol, but he figures it shows a weakness in the man's judgment."

Pearson scratched his head, still troubled that he had not found the right words to describe power at the top. "When you're sitting at the table with the boss, nothing matters but confidence. You see all those big men sitting there. God gave them just about the same IQ. If he didn't, they wouldn't be at that table in the first place. So what counts is whether you can outfox the next man in getting your point of view before the President so that it looks like the right thing to do and the right time to do it. A smart outsider can have an advantage over the bureaucrats. I've seen the Chief of Staff come to a meeting all loaded down with position papers. But they were worthless because they didn't

229

tell the boss what he needed to know—whether to give a speech, or hold a press conference, or pass a law. A good adviser never forgets the point of a meeting—that a President has to take one step at a time just like everybody else."

I sought men who had pondered the meaning of their experience with Dana. And here I came upon a curious reticence. The more intimate their involvement the more circumspect my sources proved to be. Not all were intent on concealment. Some made genuine efforts to interpret their understandings. But each one confessed his shortcoming as history's witness. Each one felt confined by the cubbyhole of his own experience.

Dana was, by all accounts, a striking figure, not only in physical bearing but in temperament. What is remembered best was his amazing capacity to remain absolutely immobile for sustained periods. It could be disconcerting to others. "There were those eyes. Icy, blue-gray. They had a curious way of withdrawing, turning inward," one remembered. "Then, with a flash of those eyes and the slightest tilt of his body he could demolish another man. I've watched some get so rattled that they forgot what they meant to say."

Dana was not a temperamental man in the ordinary sense of the word. He never stormed, never even lost his temper so far as anyone recalled. But the latitudes of temperament were there. Dana in a benign mood could light up a room of lesser men. Dana, displeased, could cast a pall without resorting to tantrums. A spinster who served as his secretary and was forever in thrall confessed to me that each morning she could predict the course of the day sim-

230

ply by the way he inflected his customary greeting: "Well, Miss Albert, what do we have on our calendar?"

Chester Dana evidently put himself through the self-training course for President's men without a hitch. He got his start while still on Pentagon duty, when he was asked to serve as a back-seat adviser at the Bretton Woods and Dumbarton Oaks conferences where postwar policy was being charted. In the words of a fellow conferee, "He had a talent for turning financial jargon into plain everyday English that everyone could understand. Pretty soon he was being called on for all sorts of advice. He wasn't pushy. Didn't speak unless spoken to. But when the President asked him to do something, wild horses couldn't get him to turn loose until he had done it."

Dana developed the habit quite early of sending the President brief memos in his own handwriting. He didn't need to stipulate that no carbon copies had been preserved for the edification of others. It became evident that neither the press nor the Washington grapevine ever learned what Dana told the President or the President told Dana. "Anytime you saw anything in the paper associating Dana with the boss, you could be sure it was the boss's work, not Dana's."

He found other subtle ways to demonstrate his loyalty. A longtime wire service reporter covering the White House described for me the time the President returned from an overseas trip in the early morning hours. "It was snowing when we landed and only a handful of officials were there to welcome him home. But Dana was there. The old man had been catching hell in the public opinion polls. You could tell he was damn appreciative. He rode Dana back to the White House in his own limousine."

231

But Dana kept his White House relations within a narrow margin of emotion. Toward the President and White House aides alike he maintained an attitude of indifference to personal gain. He was content with what life and fortune had granted him. He had no need and no desire to get into a posture of dependency. "That's a real advantage, you know," my friendly informant Pearson assured me. "Most men who come around here miss opportunity by clutching after it too hard."

Dana was always available to the President, but he conveyed the sense of remove. He conveyed it in subtle ways. One time the President asked him over for lunch, then kept him waiting till midafternoon before they sat down to the meal. After that, Dana let it be known, politely but emphatically, that he had already lunched before he came.

I collected other examples of this pull and tug—his ego against the President's. Mostly, of course, Dana gave way gracefully. He never objected to being called at any hour of the night though he was always a fitful sleeper. But he found ways of reminding the President that he had a sense of self-esteem. "When that crisis blew up in the Middle East, Dana sent word he'd like his mission to fly over on one of the Presidential planes. For some reason, the boss got contrary. Told his military aide to tell Dana the plane wasn't available. Well, old Dana said he'll wait till the plane is ready. So Dana got his plane and it strengthened his hand considerably in dealing with the Arabs not to arrive on a flying tanker."

Pearson pointed out that it would be too easy to dismiss these little clashes as pure vanity. At the rarefied levels of government, a great deal depends on nuance. A President must be constantly calculating whom he is building up and whom he is tearing down. "If he becomes too predictable, someone else ends up running things."

But President's men have to be artful too. Being taken for granted is the most deadly curse that can afflict an adviser, especially one without portfolio. It helps explain Dana's reluctance during a period when the President suddenly decided that he needed Dana right there in the White House. "It was kept quiet at the time, but the boss called in the carpenters and the decorators and had them fix up a fancy new office in the West Basement. Then he summoned Dana and told him he was a member of the staff. Dana came to work on a regular basis for a couple of months. Then he begged off. Said he could handle his affairs better working out of his own study. It baffled the boss but he couldn't get Dana to stay."

Pearson and I were meeting for drinks in the darkened bar of the Hay-Adams Hotel, built on the very site of Henry's home across from the White House. Pearson had become quite intrigued by his role as interpreter for me. "I think Dana always puzzled the President. Used to glance at him with that sudden intense look he had. As if he was wondering 'What the devil makes this fellow tick?' But he admired Dana—admired him and liked him. There's a difference. The two men were opposites in many ways. I don't think Dana had a political bone in his body and the boss had more than his share. But they did have one thing in common, I'd say—they both knew things nobody had told them. And they paid attention to their intuitions.

"I always got the feeling the boss wanted to get closer to Dana and Dana was holding back. I remember an evening

233

we were working late. When we finished, the boss told me to phone him and invite him over for a drink. Dana tried to beg off, saying he had a houseguest. The boss thought about that for a while and told me to call back and tell him to bring the houseguest along. It was all very polite and Dana brought his houseguest, but I felt he would just as soon have stayed home."

"The White House is a damned lonely place," Pearson said. "I don't know how many times I've seen the boss suddenly realize the working day was over and he had to spend the long evening in that monastery. It was even worse on weekends. I suspect he would have been inviting Dana over more often except for one thing. The boss couldn't stand Dana's wife. If there was one thing he hated, it was a bossy woman!"

A President's man, I was told, learns to develop two faces. Toward the President he must be subservient, observing the protocol of his high office. But once charged with a Presidential mandate, he must be quite aware of his prerogatives. Pearson had served as Dana's deputy during the Middle East crisis. "We got over there to find our Ambassador in way over his head and too bull-headed to admit it. Dana saw there was no time for niceties. He didn't play the Southern gentleman. Dana talked to the Arabs like a Dutch uncle. Then he got just as tough with the Israelis."

Talking to Pearson and all the other President's men, I got a perspective on both Dana and his times. He had a reputation as a man skilled in "flying by the seat of his pants." A trite expression, but it describes the kind of pioneering in foreign relations which took place after the Second World War. America's commitments abroad could be made to support or not support whatever degree of involvement the President thought expedient. Nobody had a guidebook. The only course in an unruly world was to fly by the seat of your pants.

Someday, these President's men conceded to me, the historians may be able to do an adequate job of balancing gains with losses, brilliant maneuvers with incredible blunders. But it will not be an easy story to tell, for the wars that are avoided seldom leave visible traces for the historian. The wars that have to be fought leave scars which are all too visible.

What ought to impress the historian, they argue, is the vast amount of energy expended by a very small group serving the President. They have had to take enormous gambles. At times, they have played loose with a Constitution that explicitly denies the President the power to declare war but remains silent on his power to keep the peace. Lacking doctrine, the President's men have been masters of improvisation, usually developing theory to justify their actions *after* rather than *before* the event.

And Dana was one of this group. He was a cool man in a hot crisis, but he was equally good in the long, grinding confrontations when policy moved forward an inch at a time. On two hours' notice, he had to depart town to mediate a Greek-Turkish flareup that lasted nearly six months. Day in and day out, he moved between Athens and Ankara patiently probing for signs of conciliation. According to one observer, the two sides finally worked out a truce because of sheer weariness from having to deal with Dana.

"You have no idea what an ordeal like that takes out of a man," Pearson told me. "Every step of the way he knows

235

that a single mistake and the whole thing can blow up on him. And if it does, there are not likely to be any post mortems to decide who was at fault. American foreign policy automatically gets the blame."

In charting the middle course that Stimson prophesied, there have been no rules to tell the crisis managers when to push ahead and when to take it easy, when to be hard and when soft. I find it difficult in reviewing Dana's record to label him as either hard or soft. For every episode such as Operation Snipe, when he counseled caution, there were contrary times when he urged a course of firm and even risky toughness. Many times, I was told, he left the President's table not certain whether the tactics adopted there would mean success or disaster. More than once he shared the secret misery of the insiders who went to bed at night fearing that the dawn might bring ghastly news of nuclear war.

Pearson arranged to take me on a tour of the Situation Room down in the West Basement of the White House. A smallish room. A row of various-colored telephones line one wall. A large conference table. A few maps and a screen for a slide projector. It is a quiet haven in the White House basement where the leaders convene during crisis.

In one such crisis, Pearson told me, he had the assignment to bring in the intelligence reports as fast as they arrived. He had watched each man's face as the President silently read and then silently passed the latest message around the table: each man calculating the weight and meaning of each word; each man wondering who was really at the other end of the hot line with the Kremlin—a decision-maker or maybe only a half-crazed typist; each man thinking about what it would mean if they guessed wrong. "At least I think that's what they were thinking. Nobody said. You have some mighty peculiar reactions at times like these," Pearson remarked.

Highly emotional men are not likely to get invited to that room, I was told. But still, those who were there had their ways of showing stress. The Secretary of Defense was a table-drummer. The Secretary of State never appeared to blink his eyes but he smoked one cigarette after another. Except for the boss, Dana was the most stony-faced of all. He had a habit of squeezing the bridge of his nose between his two fingers as though to relieve the pressure. And he would run his fingers through his iron-gray hair.

"Hour after hour, they sat there, not saying much, waiting for the next message. Then they'd start to figuring out the reply. Dana kept a long yellow pad before him and was always writing out his drafts in longhand. He'd read them in his deep voice and they sounded just like polished prose. Everybody would get to arguing, often as not over the form rather than the substance of the reply. I saw the boss and his top advisers spend at least ten minutes debating whether an infinitive would be clearer than a participle."

Pearson, slouched down in a chair at the head of the table in this command post, said reflectively, "That particular crisis got pretty scary before it cooled off. I remember the last stages. All the men around the table sitting there, not looking at each other, each one examining his soul. Then we got the intelligence intercepts showing the Russians were pulling back their fleet. We knew it was time to go to bed. Nobody said anything for a while. Then Dana observed in that dry way, 'Well, I only hope they lost as

237

much sleep as we did.' It wasn't particularly funny but everybody laughed like hell."

Presidential advice-giving in time of crisis, I learned, must combine the subtleness of chess with the psychology of poker. Dana played the game with the best of them. Most times, he stayed well in the background, content to help refine policies developed by the official deputies of the President. But there were other times when a "Dana gambit" became the working proposition to which even the Secretary of State paid respects. No one can recall that Dana's position ever reflected anything so rigid as a doctrine. He, like the others, simply endeavored to find the "middle course" in a thousand varying circumstances.

Dana did have an enemy and the juices of dislike brought out a quality in him that I could never entirely appreciate. The enemy's name was Arthur Cowen, a career servant in the State Department, scion of a line of distinguished public servants, originally from Connecticut but Washingtonian by long adoption. Cowen, slim, slight, horn-rim-bespectacled, wavy hair impeccably in place, met every protocol of the perfect diplomat. He was a ferocious worker and had advanced himself as much by merit as by connections. He joined the Foreign Service while still a very young man. He had wealth and he married wealth. Slowly, by the torpid processes of the Service, he moved ahead, leaping at last that mid-career hurdle which frustrates so many of the best FSO's. Cowen was an Ambassador by the time he was forty. Assistant Secretary at fifty. There was speculation, I was told, that by sixty he would advance the final stage and match the achievement of his great-great uncle who served as Secretary of State a century earlier.

238

But Arthur Cowen despised Chester Dana and the sentiment was heartily reciprocated. No one remembered who instigated the feud. No one could recall what were the precise disputations on which it grew. Both were creative, pragmatic, problem-solving men. Both were men of great civility, immense self-restraint, and total dedication to their careers. Both were firmly committed to the middle course.

Some said their wives had caused the trouble. Mrs. Cowen, from a long line of cliff dwellers in Washington, was physically quite different from Dame Dana. Small, wiry, almost emaciated looking, she wore a habitual look that she had detected something faintly distasteful in her immediate vicinity. She, like the Dame, was a driving woman and she, too, prided herself on the salon she maintained in Georgetown. Somewhere in the beginnings, so the rumor ran, one woman had deliberately snubbed the other. Perhaps that had started the chain of reciprocal slights which led to the feud.

Cowen had studied at Yale but nobody believed that college rivalry had anything to do with it. More serious were the differences between a man who had spent his whole career in government service and one who entered it laterally and high up. The careerist, I have been told, never does fully welcome the late comer to government. Both Dana and Cowen were admired by the President who could never understand why they didn't admire each other. "It amused him and annoyed him," David Pearson told me. "I think the boss got a kick out of knowing that two such smart men could be so childish. But at the same time he didn't like the idea that members of his team were cutting each other up."

The feud, though fought silently, was an enduring fact widely recognized in the upper echelons of government. Then it reached an abrupt climax. The Secretary of State called in Dana to review the East-West trade situation. It was a fairly general discussion and the Secretary seemed relieved when Dana turned down his vague invitation to serve as special adviser in this problem area. After all, East-West trade matters fell within Arthur Cowen's jurisdiction in the State Department.

But a week later the Secretary, greatly embarrassed, called back. There had been a failure of communication. It was imperative that Dana take over the East-West trade assignment as head of a task force reporting directly to the Secretary and the President. Dana would not be allowed to refuse this important mission. Obviously, the Secretary had his marching orders from the White House.

Then the story, as it has become part of Washington folklore, grows rather dramatic. In his usual quiet manner, Dana replied that he could never decline any assignment pressed on him by the President and his first deputy. But there was one stipulation he felt he had to lay down: Arthur Cowen must be stripped of the East-West trade jurisdiction. The Secretary, presumably swallowing hard, accepted Dana's terms. Not long afterward, Cowen found a graceful way of retiring from government and not too long after that both he and his wife were killed in an airplane crash while touring the South Pacific Islands.

I have listened to a good many tales of vendettas in the high places of government causing men to behave in odd ways. But this one seemed so unlikely for the Dana I knew. So vindictive. What would drive a man to exact this measure of vengeance on another man? During one of our long walks along the C & O Canal, I put this question to Dana, albeit in a less blunt form. He did not take offense. "This story has grown more melodramatic over the years," he replied with his familiar irony. "But the elemental facts are right. I did decline to get involved unless Cowen was moved out of the way. It was not a spiteful act on my part. East-West trade had been badly bungled within the State Department, and Congress was getting ready a major exposé. It would have crucified Cowen and damaged his superiors. That's why the President was so anxious to set things straight. Cowen was hoping he could pass the blame along to me. I simply outmaneuvered him."

I am convinced that this account satisfied Dana's recollections. He did not think of himself as a vindictive person. But he resolutely accepted the fact that the policy struggle at the very top can get quite rough at times. It involves men with strong personalities as well as strong likes and dislikes. It requires agility to survive. When it came to the issue of his survival versus Cowen's, Dana had no qualms about how to conduct himself.

Above all, he was a realist. The Dana Report on East-West trade, urging lowering of the barriers, was widely publicized as a dramatic break with official policy. In actual fact, Pearson assured me, it had all been pre-planned before the task force had its first meeting. "Every step of the way, Dana would bring his drafts over here for White House clearance. He knew the report would be meaningless unless the boss was on board."

Did he consciously pattern his advice to gain the President's favor? I once quoted to Dana the newspaper report

241

that he had played the President's agent, perhaps unwittingly, in scuttling "Operation Snipe." He replied, "Unwitting is a rather harsh word. I knew the President had no desire for an escapade in Africa, and I happened to agree with him." But does a President's man—I deliberately sought to put the question impersonally—ever slant his advice to say what he knows the President wants to hear? "That is a hard one to answer categorically," he replied. "No one lasts very long around the President if he is simply an echo chamber. But policies have a way of acquiring a momentum all their own. One who wishes to be useful to the President had best avoid the temptation to keep saying 'I told you so.'" Dana reflected a time before he added, "And sometimes it can end a man's usefulness when he says 'No.'" This was the closest he ever came to hinting at the events which led to his demise as a President's man.

How did it happen? It will take calculations superior to mine to isolate and identify what built the storm cloud over Dana's career. At one moment, it was no bigger than a man's hand. The next, it had effectively ended his career. What causes an ordinary storm cloud to erupt into a death-dealing hurricane? The simple answer seems to be that science doesn't have an answer. A thousand factors of time and place and chance contribute to it. A scientist told me that it would take a computer many times larger than the largest ones now available to program all the variables that make a hurricane. The mysteries of public life, as of hurricanes, remind me of Henry Adams' ironic comment: "Man may someday learn enough of his own ignorance to fall down and pray."

This much I know. The trouble began at a time when

242

crisis again had laid its chilling hand on the policymakers. The Communists were making noises in Berlin. Contrary to usual practice, the private communication channels sounded a louder alarm than the public ones. A diplomatic source, "usually reliable," sent word directly to the White House that the Soviets really meant business this time. It produced a situation in which Washington insiders were greatly agitated while the public remained comparatively serene.

But the nature of the crisis explains little so far as Dana is concerned. He had been through worse ones. And it was not unpredictable that the President, when the going got rough, should have called for his services. This time, the President explained that Dana was to play a very private role as his personal emissary to the Kremlin. There he would state in bald terms the case for preserving the *status quo* in Berlin, making clear that the U.S. was prepared to go all the way to prevent Communist takeover. Full-scale mobilization, strategic bomber alert, declaration of national emergency—the President was ready for the whole works. Then Dana was to press the message a bit further. The President was growing exceedingly weary of a situation which permitted the Communists to threaten the Free World everytime it suited their fancy. Dana could throw threats around with a freedom not permitted the official diplomats. Maybe he could push the Kremlin toward a lasting settlement of differences.

Was this mission the President's own brainchild? The passage of time has blurred memories and confused the parentage of the idea. It is entirely possible, I was told, that the President was not serious but was simply testing Dana's re-

243

actions. The President had a habit of trying out ideas that way. In any event, he quickly learned that Dana thought very little of the scheme. In soft but plainspoken fashion, Dana depicted it as a bluff that was bound to fail. Nothing would suit the Soviets more than for the U.S. to rush pell mell into mobilization, only to find itself with no place to go when Berlin quieted down. The mission would be a ploy that lacked credibility.

And that was as far as the mission got. The President, showing no outward signs of rancor, discarded the idea and nothing more was heard of it. But had his proposal and Dana's rebuff set up a tension between the two men? Did the one or the other make an offhand remark afterward which was picked up and passed along the Washington grapevine, leading to speculation about a serious dispute? Experienced observers claim that rumor in Washington can feed on far less substance than this. And rumor can quickly add to the trouble it pretends to report. This seems to be the way it happened in Dana's case. Before long, word of their disagreement reached the President's ear. He, predictably, was more than a little annoyed. Pearson gave me his version of what followed: "The boss called me in one day and asked me to have a talk with Dana. I was to get across the idea that we were pretty unhappy about these stories of a split. We couldn't understand why Dana hadn't put a stop to them. We regarded loyalty as a two-way proposition. Then I was to set up a meeting so that the boss and Dana could have a heart-to-heart talk."

How did Dana receive this reprimand? The White House aide professed to be puzzled. "He knew I wasn't saying these things on my own. But his only reaction came when I wondered out loud why he hadn't put a stop to the rumors. He kind of bristled. Said the President knew as well as he did that it didn't do any good to pay attention to rumors."

The aide thought for a moment. "Of course, he was wrong about that. The boss always paid attention to rumors."

Shortly afterward, Dana had his heart-to-heart with the President. I have tried my best to picture the two men as they entered this confrontation. For the President, it came at a time when he was heading steadily downward in public esteem. Disloyalty and suspicion of disloyalty were beginning to be widespread within his government. Everything he was trying to do was beginning to come apart. Quite possibly, he looked on the Moscow mission as a way of relieving his domestic troubles. He may have been deeply disappointed when Dana proved unwilling to accept. If the mission had succeeded, he could have leaked the story to the press and gotten the credit. If it failed, no one needed to be the wiser. At worst, the President could have repudiated Dana without undue damage to himself. These were acceptable risks for a man who saw his leadership being steadily eroded.

But the second man was unprepared to play this game. I am certain that Dana meant what he told the President in rejecting the mission. It was not the middle course. But he may also have been personally offended by the notion of being called on to play sacrificial pawn in a reckless attempt to redress the President's political fortunes. His concept of loyalty did not run that deep.

Their fateful meeting took place late in the day. While it went on, Pearson waited in the corridor outside the Oval

245

Office. Once he invented an excuse to carry a message to the President. He found the two sitting quietly before the fireplace, not speaking while he was present. He remembers how still it was. Outside, the dying sun was giving a faded color to the Rose Garden. Everything seemed unnaturally peaceful. The President read the message and then gave his familiar signal meaning he wished to be left undisturbed. A long time later, Dana emerged, white-faced, seemingly drained of all emotion. He passed by the aide without seeing him and headed down the stairway to the basement exit where his car was waiting.

Had the President ever related to Pearson what went on inside? "You don't know the boss," the aide told me. "I wouldn't dare raise the question unless he mentioned it first. He didn't and I didn't." But the White House staff didn't have to be informed that something serious had taken place. "The boss was in a foul mood. Didn't want anybody around him. I can't remember when he was ever so depressed. But he got over it. He didn't let any of his troubles keep him down for long."

The press did raise a question, the Washington *Post* reporting a few days later that the split between the President and Dana was the subject of widespread gossip in town. "We moved quickly on that one," Pearson recalled. "Dana never protested when we cooked up that meeting in the Cabinet Room and called in the photographers. He knew that it was the President's prerogative to kill the rumors." The aide had watched closely during their get-together. The two men had not exchanged a personal word.

I never got a chance to confront Dana with this insider's account. For Pearson, respectful of the conventions, had kept his silence on these details about the rupture until a new President entered the White House and Dana was in his grave. Even if it had been possible to question Dana, I doubt that I would have learned much more. Men have an amazing capacity to erase what is unpleasant from their memory books. With public men like Dana, it is as though the unpleasant never happened. The episode had become a blank page. When I did attempt once to cite the newspaper speculations, he dismissed me abruptly. "The fact is I had carried quite a burden for quite a period. It was time for me to retire and for younger men to come forward." And that, I could plainly tell, was his final word.

But, of course, it wasn't the final word for me. I had to go on worrying the ghost of Dana for a satisfactory explanation of this sad climax to his public career. Go on picking over the secondhand recollections of his friends and acquaintances, none of whom could tell the full story because it was known only to two men—and maybe not really understood by either one of them. Who ever knows the full story? When a marriage breaks up, the superficial causes usually mask the real ones. Husband and wife are often the poorest interpreters of what went wrong between them. How much more mysterious are the bonds between President and President's men.

During the aftermath of that personal crisis, Chester Dana, like the President, showed the symptoms of great stress. He departed briefly from his lifelong habits of privacy. My evidence for this comes from Henry Mann. It was Mann who had a ready explanation when I related to him what the White House aide had told me. "My dear boy, you can't print a word of it. But the answer is simple: our dear,

247

departed friend Chester experienced a massive crisis of confidence."

I was angered by Mann's certainty. How could he be so sure about this mystery that plagued me and a good many others who knew Dana as well as he did? "My lips are sealed," he answered in his smug way. "But take my word for it." I retorted heatedly that I was not prepared to accept such a vital fact on faith alone. Finally, Mann relented a little. "You mustn't breathe a word of it," he told me self-importantly. "Chester Dana came to see me that night directly after he left the President. He was a deeply troubled man and he confided in me. He had lost confidence. He had lost faith. He was no longer capable of serving as the President's man."

XXVII

ONE hot summer day during our early months as lovers, Pascal and I biked up the towpath of the C & O Canal which her father and I had so often walked along. It was a day of almost savage blues and greens. Pascal, wearing whipcord jodhpurs and a skimpy T-shirt, urged me farther and farther until, exhausted and perspiring freely, we came to a stone lock-keeper's cottage, long since abandoned. Lord, she was lovable that day! With mysterious finger to lips, she led me tiptoeing around the cottage until we found a way to penetrate its cool darkness. There, inside, we played "Ladies Lead Out" with Pascal, kneeling astride my hips, making me the passive participant in the fierce jousting.

There were a thousand postures and a thousand dreams. But I found that the larger dream, drowning out the rest, was of Pascal when she gave me a quick smile, or, eyes bright, seemed for one moment to regard me as more than prize stud.

At what combustion point in sexual relations does lust

249

take on the purer properties of love? Or does it happen that way for normal men and women? All I can record in the saga of Bohun's affair with the daughter of the Dana family is that lust came first but slowly there followed what seemed to be a stirring of deeper, nobler passions.

For Bohun at least. As the months passed, while I pretended to perform my biographical mission, I kept a contact with sanity by concentrating all my capacity for desire on this young woman. And gradually over time desire became less and less a craving for physical coupling. Asleep and awake, I found myself dreaming of Pascal, but not just of the hot, aching moments with body against body like two tight-strung bows. More and more, desire became a yearning to know, to be with, to exchange intimate thoughts and feelings.

What a mixed-up tale this is in the telling! That I, the male animal, should be seeking something more than sex and she, the female, should so jealously withhold everything but her body. But over time it seemed to me that Pascal's tight system of defenses began to weaken. Until—or so it seemed to me—Pascal began to care.

It started that night beneath the Calvert Street Bridge. Her outburst about Peter marked an opening intimacy that I was quick to explore. We probed the raw wound left by her brother's suicide, and the hurt she felt toward her father. The love of brother and the hate of father came as strange experiences to me, an only child who felt at worst only condescension toward my parents. But for Pascal these were burning emotions that had grown no less real with the passage of time. I came to sympathize with her feeling for her brother. There was much about her tale of Peter's boyhood

250

enthusiasms and his uncertainties that I could understand. He had been a curious offspring of the chaste union between Chester and Emily Dana. Within him there must have surged the nervous soul of an artist. He had displayed quite early strong attraction to music. A Mozart piano concerto, Pascal told me, could reduce him to tears. But he was a flawed artist, for he had no aptitude as musician. Lacking drive and self-discipline, he seemed created to serve as appreciative audience for other people's talents.

While I could understand her love for Peter, I found it impossible to sort out the mingled emotions that resolved themselves into hatred of parent. Evidently the daughter had never felt any warmth toward the intense, driven mother. Still, I suspected the possibility of deep love for the father. Somewhere along the way something had blighted that love. As best I could gather, there was no single incident to bring disillusion—not until the tragedy of Peter's death. But during all their years of growing up, Chester Dana's drives had been directed toward other objects than his children. He had been an overly good provider and a sparing taskmaster. Perhaps too sparing. Perhaps too uncaring. That is the only way I can account for it, unless I have not asked the hard questions about Pascal. Unless I have refused to face up to the possibility that she was the bad seed who found it in her nature to blame her father.

All that opening summer of our intimacy, I nursed each sign that my relations with Pascal had progressed beyond the tactile stage. In the fall, after she returned to school, we conspired to take a long weekend trip exploring the North Carolina coastline as far south as Ocracoke Island, masquerading as man and wife. I remember with how much

251

hope I set out on this tryst. For once, I would have uninterrupted time with Pascal, time to explore the other things we might share besides sex. But the weekend was a disaster. Bleak, premature hurricane weather made the beaches miserable and cast a chill on our spirits. The fisherman's lodge at Ocracoke had drab and drafty rooms. Every squeak of the bedsprings resounded through the dismal corridors.

When we descended that Sunday morning for a greasy breakfast, all the male eyes lasciviously followed us to our table and sudden silences greeted our attempts at conversation. When we finally made our departure, a long-jawboned old desk clerk gave me a knowing wink and chortled, "That's a mighty frisky little bride you've got." I felt embarrassment mixed with shame.

But the real failure of that weekend could not be blamed on weather or lodging. I came back convinced that my pathetic efforts at love were destined to get nowhere. Someone was at fault either in the giving or the receiving. I began to feel that my nonphysical relations with Pascal were akin to a jujitsu contest, my every lunge turned into a sprawl by her countertactics. The worst of it was that she seemed unaware—completely unaware and unconcerned.

The winter was marked with growing misery on my part. There were weeks on end when I, resolved that disengagement was my only weapon, pretended to be icily indifferent to her. It demanded every conceit of which I was capable. As the days dragged by, the tension became unbearable for me; but so far as I could tell, she scarcely noticed. All it took was one signal from her, one unexpected visit to my lonely gatekeeper cottage, and my reserves vanished. Then afterward, the torment began again.

That second spring there came a breaking point. It happened in an almost casual way on a night that was near the anniversary of our first assignation. Thinking to be clever, I suggested to Pascal that we might revisit the summer house and re-enact our earlier adventure. "Nothing has changed," I said in a strained attempt at humor. "I am still the kept biographer learning to endure the snotty offspring." But it was the wrong thing to say. She replied very quietly: "Something has changed. You have come to expect too much of me. And I—— too little of you. Maybe it's time we faced reality." I tried gently to tease her out of it, but she had already reached an inner resolve. I had a cold, sickly feeling when we parted that night, no amount of urging having served to change her mind. She did not come round again.

I find it difficult to think about what followed. As the days passed into weeks, my separation from this girl brought all the symptoms familiar to an addict taken off his drug. I grew quite wild with anxiety and frustration. Physical longing returned in a fresh torrent and I relived in my imagination each experience. My imagination being what it is, the reliving gave an ecstasy to this lust greater than was there in the first place. Why, I kept asking in my misery, had I not been content to accept Pascal as I found her? As weeks changed into months, I even found myself, as I watched the distant girl, beginning to have doubts that we had once been intimate.

Then there came another Dana party, only this time she

253

had other dinner partners. One was an aging Senator, somewhat paunchy, his sole distinction being a mane of snow-white hair. The other—and he was the target of my purest hatred—was a debonair young Congressman with a well-earned reputation, I had heard, as a chaser after women. Soon after the meal, I feigned a headache and retired to my room. But suspicion's torture was too great. Something led me that evening, pulled me along the long winding path amid the nostalgic springtime smells. I found myself outside the garden house. That same moon lighted the night as it had the year before. And, as I peered through the window, that same chaise mattress was on the floor and the same girl was engaged, *flagrante delicto*. In the first numb of emotion I still had time to contemplate, amid the tangle of clothes and half-bared limbs, how graceless is the sex act. Then a second shock blanked out my critical faculties. For the other participant in this all-too-familiar sport was not the debonair Congressman but the aging, paunchy, white-maned Senator.

How to explain what happened next? I've always been fascinated by men's efforts to account for their behavior during periods of great personal stress. Better to leave it untold. There is a point beyond which man sheds the skin of civilized conduct, when he reverts to a state of nature. This was one time in my life when Bohun, the voyeur, and Bohun, the actor, became the same man. During the wild night that followed, for once I was not conscious of looking over my own shoulder.

My one desire was to inflict hurt—hurt on myself since I was not quite animal enough to interrupt Pascal's tryst and inflict the hurt on her. It was utterly irrational. It makes no

254

sense in the telling these many years later. I left the Dana home that evening determined to destroy myself. But I lacked the courage. Instead, in a downtown Washington strip joint where lonely servicemen watch mammoth-bosomed whores dance upon the bar, I drank myself to stupefaction. Later on, I recall only brief flashes of consciousness in a dingy hotel room. One moment on the bed stands out clearly as the whore exposed her flatulence to my rage. "Take it easy, honey" were the last words I heard before easing into oblivion.

Next morning, alone in this hotel-room purgatory, I suffered the combined assaults of guilt and nausea. The two Bohuns had returned, each blaming the other for misconduct during the night. But one thing remaining unchanged was my pure hatred for Pascal and, through her, the whole Dana household in which I had become so hopelessly trapped. My single resolve was to break free once and for all.

By late afternoon, I had recovered enough composure and health to face the Danas. But my carefully rehearsed story meant to terminate the biographical mission never got delivered. For back at the mansion, at the top of the long stairway, I came upon Dame Dana and she, grimly controlled, had another story to tell me first. Sometime during that malevolent night her husband had been felled with a severe blood clot pressing on the brain. It was by no means certain that he would survive the day. Would I be willing to lay aside my writing chores and help out during the crisis? Standing there in the twilight, miserable and defeated, I mumbled a few confused words of sympathy and obeyed her summons.

255

XXVIII

DANA did survive the day. He survived and lived on nearly another year, mute, paralyzed, more vegetable than man. The doctors worked their miracles to keep body and breath together even though all manifestations of the brain had vanished. It is such an awful hoax they perpetrate on mortality. No one can really know what it means to the victim himself. There, in his tomb of flesh, does he still cling willingly to his feeble heartbeat?

Of this period, my notebooks record not a word. Memory is vivid enough of the once-commanding face grown shriveled. Even those eyebrows had lost their bristle, now having to surmount a vacant stare. We never knew for sure whether our voices reached his inner vault. If they did, he gave no answering sign. For nearly a year, we continued to play the charade that he was among us but he would not or could not play. I became his regular reader, plowing endlessly through newspapers, magazines, and books in hopes of stimulating by some chance phrase a faint flicker of life.

But my words fell into a bottomless canyon and there was not even an echo.

Why did I stay on? It should be clear by now that I am hopeless when it comes to understanding motivations, least of all my own. Love? Certainly not. During those final months I came partly to loathe the dying Dana even as I had almost loved the living one. Guilt? That may have played a part. I, who had been about to abandon the whole enterprise, must have felt that playing nursemaid served as a form of expiation. Perseverance? Not at all. With Dana's stroke, my notebooks came to an end. Now the man himself could tell me nothing and I lacked energy to go on searching for answers to the mystery that had shrouded his life. Lacked the energy and for a time even the interest. I would serve as Dana's nursemaid. But the dream of the biography had died that dread night.

Did I stay on because of Dame Dana? Perhaps she contributed a motive. Never really liking her while her husband was in good health, I soon developed a grudging affection for her now that he was helpless. She bowed so gallantly to this fate. Overnight, the Dana home was transformed into a sick ward, and she devoted her every waking hour to him. Until his death, she never accepted an outside engagement. All her busy-busy causes and social involvements were allowed to lapse. As I watched, I soon lost certainty of the one thing I had once been certain of. Perhaps there was a love between these two that went very deep even if it never revealed itself in word or gesture. One more proof of how Bohun, the biographer, had failed. And suddenly I realized that Dame Dana had known of her husband's inner crisis. That was why she conceived the idea of the biography and enlisted me as its author. She had hoped to save his self-esteem and thereby to save him.

And what about Pascal? Could I possibly have lingered in the desperate hope that we might resume our miserable liaison? I refused to believe that this was so. She seldom visited her father's bedside and when she did I invented excuses to absent myself. I never mentioned what I had seen that night but secretly hoped that my demeanor would reveal my knowledge to her. She knew. Of course, she must have known. But she was able to play this stoic game far better than I. During the long year, there was no exchange of word or look to indicate that we had once been lovers —no, not lovers—that we had once so freely fornicated.

During that year of death watch, Dame Dana and I shared all the times of day. The early morning dreariness. The vast boredom of afternoon, lunch past, and hours stretching unendingly till suppertime. Twilight was the best time. We shared our favorite drink, undiluted sour mash on ice. A comfortable time. The eeriness of gloaming. A time of day when the semi-light and liquor loosened one's tongue. Then the Dame lost her habitual tenseness.

All the while we could hear the breathing of our patient in his adjoining bedroom. How heavily he breathed. Great gulps at life. I had no idea that he had that much lung capacity. It set a rhythm for our conversations. And it provided the interludes for our long silences.

Twelve months of waiting for death! Now, five years later, it is hard to remember how I endured this terrible stretch of time. We could not know that it would last so long. Dame Dana was reconciled as much as I that her husband was beyond recall. But we could not be certain how

258

long the agony might stretch on. The doctors offered no hope and no alternatives. So I sat there with the old woman, watching her calm in this final act of her life with Chester Dana. Together we watched the endless turn of days through each of the seasons Dana had loved so well. Through all the range of colors—through lush greens and blues, crimson-goldens, infinite grays, budding yellows. Inside, the monotonous whiteness of the sick room. We listened to that regular, deep breathing of a strong man whose body, torn from any ties of will or spirit, still clung doggedly to life.

I cannot pretend that devotion to duty kept me near that bedside, for I had passed beyond any notion of martyrdom. I stayed, let me be honest, because I could not summon the spirit to leave. Deep in my consciousness I knew that life went on in this lonely city. I knew that someday I must return to the land of the living, pick up plans for a career, figure out a new way to go on living. But this knowledge failed to serve as goad. So I stayed and came near myself to feeling the finality of death. Not the abrupt death of the brain which had overtaken Dana, but the slow yielding of any desire to exist as a separate being. There was no terror in this. It was the nearest I've ever been to true religion— this awareness that there comes a time when the nagging desires which make men struggle for identity can give way to a greater desire for oblivion. It must happen at last to every man who is not struck down by sudden malady.

During Dana's moribund state, his wife gradually revealed more and more of herself to me. She had far greater sensitivity than I suspected. She had recognized early the conditions of living with a successful man. During the Wall

259

Street years, it meant becoming accustomed to great aloneness—but aloneness, she told me, had been her natural condition since early childhood. Later, after the concentrated work of his Pentagon years, Dana had arranged a way of life that did not demand such sustained physical separations. His office was in his home much of the time. But by then the habits of separation—mental, even spiritual—had become deep-rooted.

It was a condition she accepted resolutely and which she saw no way of avoiding for their children as they grew up in the driven, lonely world of Washington. Not that Dana didn't love his children, not that he lacked a father's concern for their problems of growing up. But the priority of his concerns always forced parenthood into second place. She had seen it happen time and again. There had been the time Peter was summarily expelled from prep school. She had known then that the boy was in desperate need of a father's understanding. Understanding and, yes, discipline which only a father could provide. Circulating his crude efforts at pornography had been such a pitiable offense and the punishment of expulsion was obviously fashioned to solve the problems of the prep school rather than of a troubled boy. But Dana had departed that very week for his crisis mission in Greece and Turkey—a mission that stretched out more than half a year. By the time he returned, Peter's course was set. On her own initiative she had searched out the military academy and consigned him to its strict regimen. Had that been a fateful mistake? Who could know at the time? Who could know even when her son lay in his grave?

During these quiet communions, I found the dour old

woman quite unsparing of herself. Why had not the mother better served as father substitute? This was a question she must have asked herself many, many times. Something in the stern breeding of New England caused the failure of communication, the failure of caring which cut her off so completely from her children. It is possible that the unloving family life she was accustomed to as a child had contained strengths which were not transplantable to Washington. Hers had been a large family in a stable community with patterns of tranquility handed on from one generation to the next. Even the tragic automobile accident which had killed her brother could not destroy these patterns. But neither Peter nor Pascal inherited this tranquility. They grew up in a city wracked with war and rumors of war. And their father was off at the battlefronts even when he was at home.

We talked of Peter. But there was the tacit admission that Pascal, too, was part of the same conversation. The mother never indicated by word or expression whether she knew of her daughter's nymphomania. But I believe she understood that at some formative stage in her life, Pascal ceased to grow in grace and beauty and love, instead transforming her body into a mechanical instrument for the sole satisfaction of sex. Dame Dana understood that Pascal as much as Peter had suffered a suicide of the spirit. Life was for her a succession of body contacts. Without the capacity to care, sex became merely a rub.

During those long, long days and nights near the dying man's bedside, I at last felt certain that I had penetrated the mask of Dana's wife. I learned that her crudity, her intensity were simply the disguises that she had fashioned to per-

261

mit her to get through life. So was her relentless search for busy, busy causes. And though I cannot prove it—such speculations are not susceptible to proof—I am convinced that given a different man with a different career she would have emerged a totally different woman. Not necessarily a better woman, but at least a woman with a different mask.

But she uttered no word of regret for the life with Dana. She had anticipated what it was to be like living with a man who had the compulsion to excel. She also knew well before their marriage that he was destined to continue his life as an interior man, never really sharing with her or with anyone his whole self. She had made her bed. I never had reason to believe that she regretted the loneliness she found there.

Had she ever got behind her husband's mask? I believe she did. Though she did not share his interior life, she understood and accepted it. I believe she assayed the strengths and weaknesses of this bronzelike public figure. And she deeply felt the crisis that caused his retreat from public life.

On a long dark evening while Dana breathed heavily in the next room, she tried to convey a wife's understanding of what it was like during those years at his prime. She knew that the President had not been fond of her. Perhaps he sensed a rival for her husband's energies. Perhaps she simply was not cast for wife of a President's man. She accepted this fate philosophically. It had meant one more separation from her husband.

Still she knew what her husband was going through. He had been, she said, like one trying to sweep back the sea with each wave of crisis remorselessly following the next one. Trying to sweep back the sea had wearied her man.

262

Sea-sweeping had finally broken her man. Though she did not say precisely these words, the meaning was not lost on me. And yet there was no bitterness. It had been his destiny. Any other career besides sea-sweeping would have offered no escape, for being bored can be worse for a man than being broken.

Through Dame Dana's eyes, I saw that her husband had been an idealist. He had made his way through the system; indeed, compromised with it when he had to. He did not wave his idealism on a banner. It might have been better for him if he had. Dana might have survived if he had shared his hopes and doubts and premonitions. Kept pent up inside, they created the terrible pressures. He found himself caught in an unbearable tension between idealism and cynicism. This was the wife's evaluation of her husband.

By now, the intimacy we shared at Dana's deathbed had carried us far beyond the bounds of our original contract. She told me things that I am certain she had never intended for the biography. Possibly now that he was beyond recall, beyond reburnishing, she no longer cared what the book contained. She may even have sensed that the biography would die with Dana. She desperately needed someone she could talk to now that the purpose of her life had been withdrawn.

We moved at last to the final intimacy. Had she been the wife that Dana would—or should—have wanted? I could tell that this, too, was not the first time she had weighed that question. What could she answer? Perhaps another woman—a softer, gentler woman—could have provided the surcease from care that might have helped him to endure the strain. For a long while, Dame Dana wavered be-

263

fore she made one more stern resolve. Then while we could still hear the heavy gasps at life from her husband in the nearby room, she looked me straight in the eye and announced in the harsh flat voice, "There was another woman, you know. Perhaps it would be a good idea if you find out from her."

I remember even now my admiration for this proud old woman; that she should have to be the one who made this revelation. Why had no one else even hinted at such a scandal in Dana's life? Not even Mann. I do not know the answer to this except that great men, once removed from positions of power, acquire a special protection in the public memory, and especially in the memory of their friends. We shelter them in retirement even as we crucify them while they are in service. But Dame Dana was prepared to be honest. I could sense the deep-down hurt and frustration she must have felt, knowing her husband was involved with this other woman. Not knowing—only suspecting—how deep and how lasting would be the involvement. It had come to an abrupt end at the time of Peter's death, she told me with a hint of bitterness.

I felt irresolute about prying further into Dana's past. Curiosity finally drove me to it. She lived in Kalorama, less than a mile from the Dana estate, her tiny townhouse set amid the large embassy residences. Her rooms had an appearance of gentle disarray exactly in keeping with her own appearance. She was gentle and soft and blonde. The years had added a faded quality to her portrait. She was everything Dame Dana was not. Despite her years a strong sexuality permeated this woman, exuding its fragrance with her every movement. She seemed a serene woman. She bore fascinating resemblances to the Raeburn painting which Dana and I used to visit. Even with the difference of our ages, I could understand why a weary man would want to visit here.

She was cordial and entirely at ease about my request for an interview. Yes, Dana came to her home quite frequently during one period, often dropping by unannounced at the end of a long day. No, he never seemed to mind whether there were others present. She had run a small salon of her own and Dana was by no means the only caller. I thought I detected a quiet pride that she had been able to attract so many men in high places over so many years. For one with my puritanical streak, it seemed a strange salon. Listening to this faded blonde, I realized that my preconceptions were far too strait-laced, far too shaped by the sniggering notions of my youth.

Feeling a schoolboy's rednecked embarrassment, I managed to blurt out my surprise that Dana's involvement had not received more publicity in this scandal-hungry city. "It was no secret and it was no scandal," she replied calmly. "I don't think Chester ever even considered that. Therefore no one else did." Perhaps something in my face showed I was not convinced. She seemed a trifle impatient at being obliged to add: "You make a mistake if you think that sex was involved. I have had lovers before and since. But what Chester Dana needed was not sexual love. He was a deeply troubled man. He was a tragic man. What he needed and what I tried to give him was a chance to lay aside his troubles." I came away convinced that sex was not involved, though this could scarcely comfort Dame Dana for the intimacy had been just as great.

265

Like Lady M, this soft and sensitive woman had applied the word *tragic* to Dana. And at last I think I have begun to understand what they meant by it. All his life, Chester Dana was accustomed to the sure feel of success. Not the quick heady triumph that has become celebrated as success these days. In school, in business, and in government, Dana measured and found success the steady way. He did not triumph over handicap for he had no handicaps worth mentioning. He simply made the fullest use of his capacities in a life affording them scope. That is the Greek formula for happiness. And I'm confident that Dana did know happiness most of the time.

To devote every ounce of one's energy and intellect to the highest endeavors of statescraft can be every bit as satisfying as to devote those same resources to a passionate love affair. A love affair must necessarily be limited by the capacities of its two participants. It takes extraordinarily single-purposed people to be consumed by a love affair for more than finite periods or to find in it the ultimate fulfillment. Statescraft is another thing. It demands all a man's energies, all his resources of mind and body, all his habits of command and persuasion and more. Watch a first-rank statesman at work and you get an inkling of the ecstasy he feels. Usually he hides ecstasy behind a solemn mask. But it is there. What is ecstasy but the sense of finding oneself seized by something bigger than oneself? Like the joy that comes to a young person who first finds himself moving to the rhythms of the dance. Like the uncontrollable giving of the lover. Like the philosopher's thrill when he is transported beyond the limits of his mind into pure creative thought. Most of all, there is ecstasy for the man who finds

266

himself turned into a creative instrument for his nation.

Then when does such ecstasy have an end? For many men it never does. They go on reliving the memory of it long after their capacity has faded. It is as true of statesmen as of lovers. They spend their dying years recalling those moments when they were on the cutting edge of action. And sometimes you watch worn-out statesmen making pathetic efforts at a comeback even as you watch tired old lovers going through grotesque efforts at seduction.

But Dana was different. For him, I have realized, ecstasy reached its ending while he was still caught in its transports. Then why? It is because ecstasy requires something more —a premonition of successful outcome to one's endeavors. The lover who is incapable of the final act of love—who knows for certain he is incapable—loses the capacity for ecstasy. Sex itself becomes a tiresome exercise. The fear of failure dries up his juices. To persist, such a man may become a satyr, but he can never be an ecstatic lover.

So it is with the statesman, I concluded. I saw that Dana's intuition had been too powerful an influence over his career. He was, in truth, a mystic. And just as other mystics have been driven by soul's torment into the wilderness away from the contamination of a world where they can find no redemption from evil, Dana sought his own seclusion.

XXIX

MY hero, Henry Adams, despite his professed humility, was a presumptuous man. In his *Education,* he wrote of his arrival in Washington: "The first step, of course, was the making of acquaintance, and the first acquaintance was naturally the President. . . ." For me this was the last step, and then only after the President had long vacated his office. It occurred after I had begun this attempt to make an accounting for my years with Dana. It took place in the hotel suite where the former leader, back in Washington for a political-party celebration, was holding court with his President's men of bygone days. Time had performed a winnowing and there were only Mr. Loyalties around him. They clustered close and regarded me with suspicious, half-shuttered eyes, wary of the intruder that I was. But he had granted the interview readily, professing to be happy to honor in any way he could the memory of his old friend Dana, now deceased.

I went to the interview full of apprehensions. How would

I behave in the presence of a man who had been at the very center of the web of power? But once there in the congested hotel room, with the ex-President seated in a high wing-backed chair, I found my fears had vanished. I regarded this leader shed of the power and perquisites of office and was struck by how relaxed he looked. Adams had written of an earlier President that he "appeared as an intermittent energy, immensely powerful when awake, but passive and plastic in repose." Maybe it is a condition common to Presidents and ex-Presidents. This one still showed the habits of command—of swift, sure judgment. He motioned me to a chair next to him and for a time his satraps drew away. Being President, I thought to myself, leaves its enduring mark on a man. Or is it merely in the eye of his beholder?

What does an ex-President brood about—a man who has departed office amid a cacophony of catcalls from his people? Does he take comfort from history's reassurance that this is the customary exit? Or does he relive a thousand times each fateful step along his road of misadventures? Somehow I doubt that he suffers all the past torments, for his agony would be too conspicuous to hide from public view. A man who has stood so much pressure must have the inner strength to endure its withdrawal.

But what does a former President brood about? Simón Bolívar surveyed his own lifetime of leadership in Brazil and concluded mournfully: "I plowed furrows in the ocean." But as I watched the bonhomie of the ex-President surrounded by his loyal few, I could detect no such pessimism. He sat there, the flush of leadership still on his face. He looked like a man at peace with himself. Perhaps he

269

was a better philosopher than Bolívar, for surely a leader cannot measure his own work in his own time.

I had told myself that this interview would be meaningful, *the* meaningful episode of my investigations: the final clue to the Dana mystery. But I knew better as soon as I entered the congested hotel room. This dogged old leader had been accustomed to a career of concealment against inquiries more persistent than mine. Compared to Dana's, the ex-President's mask was many times more impenetrable. He patiently brushed aside my attempts to probe the break between them. He gently informed me that he never made a practice of remembering ill of any man. And though I suspected his benignity, I understood that he wanted to believe it was true. I wished so much to explore with him not just the specific twists and turns of Chester Dana's downfall but the larger problem that it raised. I yearned to ask: "Mr. President, if power corrupts, as Lord Acton says, what happens to a man who is a bystander too long on the periphery of power?" There, in his benign presence, and in the presence of his hard-eyed acolytes, I was incapable of such a pretentious question. We talked instead of trivialities.

Then it was time to depart. As I neared the door, the ex-President seemed to sense that something still was lacking. He called across the room in final summary, "Chester Dana was the wisest man I ever knew." Then, while I stood waiting, he repeated his words, slightly amending them. "You can quote me on that, Bohun: Chester Dana was just about the deepest thinker—and the most farsighted—I ever knew." Even now I cannot be sure whether he intended these words as undiluted praise. Did he mean, per-haps, too deep for public life? Too farsighted?

Despite my disappointment, I came away from this visit with one more man of flesh and blood to reckon with. See-ing the ex-President at close hand, I could not dismiss the possibility that his break with Dana had been an accident based on purely human failings. So many unpredictables would have affected the President's behavior—the un-certain state of his bowels that day, the incessant nag of problems tugging at his sleeve, the erratic flow of fact and rumor that fed his prejudices, and, above all, the constant need to make judgments—snap judgments about another man's loyalty. As I watched this man who had held the high office, I saw that he was deeply human.

Dana, too, had had human problems that could have shaped his behavior during his crisis with the President. It happened not so long after Peter's death. Shortly before, I learned from Pascal, she had visited her brother's room and found, hidden away behind his books, a diary. It con-tained a tight, scribbled entry, eloquent in its brevity: "I always loved my father and wanted to be like him. But I failed him all along the way. Now my final failure . . . the bad seed returns to earth."

She had carried the tenderly vindictive note straight to her father. He read it in her presence and, for once, the austere man appeared overcome by an emotion resembling grief. For a long time he sat quite still while she, helpless in her own grief, sat nearby. There had been no exchange, simply each one quietly suffering. Finally, he had asked, "Does your mother know of this?" and she shook her head,

271

struggling to swallow the lump of sorrow. "I do not believe it can possibly lighten her burden to share it with her. Will you help me keep it a secret?" She nodded as he tore out the page and carefully folded and placed it in an inner pocket of his wallet.

How wounding had been this tragedy for Dana? He may well have wondered whether he could communicate with Kremlin leaders when he could not even reach his own son. I, who have known the failure of my love for Pascal Dana, have no means of measuring what happens to a father whose love has failed.

But I cannot be content with this patchwork explanation of Dana's downfall. There is a larger pattern to be traced. I recall what Henry Adams wrote so many years ago about the "Southern Statesmen" who preceded Dana in Washington: "None doubted. All were great men; some, no doubt, were greater than others; but all were statesmen and all were supported, lifted, inspired by the moral certainty of rightness. To them the universe was serious, even solemn, but it was their universe. . . ." Adams argued that "this self-assurance not only gave Andrew Johnson the look of a true President, but actually made him one."

Self-assurance was the guiding principle not only for the Southern Statesmen but for most politicians who reached eminence in the nation's capital; not only for Andrew Johnson but for all who became "true" Presidents. None have doubted. All have been inspired by the moral certainty of rightness. *Doubt,* like cynicism, has been the deadly sin that could never be allowed to contaminate American leadership.

Chester Dana, I have concluded with a final finality that

272

leaves me breathless, was indeed doubt's victim. His crisis with the President was the culmination of a growing crisis of doubt. Not doubt in the President. Not doubt in the wisdom of the course our nation had set for itself since the Second World War. No, Dana had come to doubt whether this nation was capable of maintaining the consistent conduct and steady uses of power to stay the middle course. Perhaps he, like Henry Adams, even doubted that the future was to be shaped by man's reason. He faced "the inevitable isolation and disillusionment of a really strong mind." This did not happen suddenly. For Dana, it must have been a lifetime in happening.

Though Dana was a man of this century who was born to certainty and who died with doubt, he was not Everyman. How do other men in public life overcome their doubts? They overcome, so far as I can observe, by remarkably simple acts of faith. Like loyalty. Everywhere in Washington you see men swearing loyalty to someone or something. Men who call themselves liberals or conservatives can be just as irrational in their loyalties as party hacks or political henchmen. Rationality has nothing to do with it. Loyalty is an emotion. "My country right or wrong" is the spirit of loyalty. And you can substitute for country "my President," "my boss," "my party," "my credo," or simply "my way of looking at life." When a man starts to question loyalty, he is in danger. But Dana could never manage that kind of loyalty.

With his psychic vision, I believe Dana recognized that his personal crisis was forerunner of a public crisis of doubt. He must have foreseen the great dark shadow of doubt that would loom over this nation; foreseen the coming storm of doubt that would threaten the nation's politics and destroy its public men. As in the past, he must have had presentiments of mass delusions and crowd hysteria. So Dana took the course he had once before followed when the nation was headed into bankruptcy: quietly, stoically, he abandoned the ship of state. This time, as an act of self-preservation, he privately confided his fears to a publicist who could, if the necessity arose, provide a public explanation. For Dana must have known that the President would be lastingly resentful of Dana's doubt. The President would be duty-bound to continue the course, to be ruthless toward anyone who undermined his own certainties.

For the President, the choice is clear-cut in time of crisis. Against all else he must peddle furiously to keep up the momentum of government. Action—or even the mere appearance of action—becomes his obsession. Not knowing what the future holds, not certain he can affect the future, he acts. But for other men, including advisers to the President like Dana, crisis can mark the explosion point in the accumulation of doubt. Crisis can be a time of agony. Crisis can mean the loss of faith.

Now I have exorcized my devils and I am ready to start again on my biographical labor. Only two restraints stand in my way. First I must be entirely certain that the affair with Pascal is finished. It will be a hard choice for I still feel at times the sudden choke of memories. But I know now with the fierce clarity of five years hindsight that there can be no happiness where there is no caring. I am done with Pascal Dana, I hope.

There is still a harder choice. For I must choose between

the two Henrys—between Henry Adams viewing disillusionment as the inevitable romance and tragedy of statesmanship, and Henry Stimson who declared at career's end that the only deadly sin is cynicism. This means I will be choosing between the man who withdrew from battle and the man who stayed his failing course. I must choose because the biographer has to deliver history's verdict. But it will not be an easy choice for me.

Can I prove that this was the real confrontation between Dana and the President? Of course, I can't. How does one prove the loss of faith? As Dana's would-be biographer, I have been obliged to make the mighty leap of imagination. Dana never did expose himself to me. He was laid in his coffin with his soul still inviolate. And though I loved him for his greatness, I hated him for what he did to me and to my illusions about myself—about my capacity to understand another man and to describe him so that someone else would understand. To accomplish our separate fulfillments, we each had contrary needs. Long before he died, it was clear that Dana's needs had prevailed over mine.

275

ABOUT THE AUTHOR

Douglass Cater was for many years the Washington Editor of *The Reporter,* where he gained wide recognition for the clarity and intelligence of his writing and won the George Polk and Front Page Awards. Mr. Cater served four and a half years in the White House as Special Assistant to President Lyndon Johnson—among the longest lived of the "President's Men." He is the author of several distinguished nonfiction books on government, notably *Power in Washington* and *The Fourth Branch of Government.* With Marquis Childs, he co-authored *Ethics in a Business Society.* Mr. Cater, a native of the South who studied at Harvard, lives in Washington, D.C. where he is now devoting full time to writing. *Dana: The Irrelevant Man* is his first book of fiction.